OXFORD*modernPlayscripts*

○ ○ ○ ○ ○ ○ ○ ○ ○ ○ ○   ○ ○ ○ ○ ○

Troy 24

David Calcutt

OXFORD
UNIVERSITY PRESS

OXFORD
UNIVERSITY PRESS

Great Clarendon Street, Oxford OX2 6DP

Oxford University Press is a department of the University of Oxford.
It furthers the University's objective of excellence in research,
scholarship, and education by publishing worldwide in

Oxford   New York

Auckland   Cape Town   Dar es Salaam   Hong Kong   Karachi
Kuala Lumpur   Madrid   Melbourne   Mexico City   Nairobi
New Delhi   Shanghai   Taipei   Toronto

With offices in

Argentina   Austria   Brazil   Chile   Czech Republic   France   Greece
Guatemala   Hungary   Italy   Japan   Poland   Portugal   Singapore
South Korea   Switzerland   Thailand   Turkey   Ukraine   Vietnam

Troy 24 © David Calcutt 2007

Activity section © Jenny Roberts 2007

The moral rights of the author have been asserted

Database right Oxford University Press (maker)

First published 2007

British Library Cataloguing in Publication Data

Data available

ISBN: 978 0 19 832101 9

10 9 8 7 6

Typeset by Fakenham Photosetting, Fakenham, Norfolk

Printed by Bell and Bain Ltd., Glasgow

Troy 24 was first performed by Raw Talent Youth Theatre in February 2007.

Acknowledgements

Extract from The Iliad of Homer translated by Robert Fitzgerald (Oxford
World Classics, 1984, 1998), reprinted by permission of the Estate of Robert
Fitzgerald.

Artwork is by Bob Moulder/Graham Cameron Illustration.

Cover photograph is courtesy of Alamy Limited.
P.106: Wikimedia

Contents

General Introduction

With a fresh, modern look, this classroom-friendly series boasts an exciting range of authors – from Pratchett to Chaucer – whose works have been expertly adapted by such well-known and popular writers as Philip Pullman and David Calcutt. We have also divided the titles available (see page 112) into subcategories – OXFORD *Classic Playscripts* and OXFORD *Modern Playscripts* – to make it even easier for you to think about titles – and periods – you wish to study.

Many teachers use OXFORD *Playscripts* to study the format, style, and structure of playscripts with their students; for speaking and listening assignments; to initiate discussion of relevant issues in class; to meet the Drama objectives of the Framework; as an introduction to the novel of the same title; and to introduce the less able or willing to pre-1914 literature.

At the back of each OXFORD *Playscript*, you will find a brand new Activity section, which not only addresses the points above, but also features close text analysis, and activities that provide support for underachieving readers and act as a springboard for personal writing. Furthermore, the new Activity sections now match precisely the Framework Objectives for Teaching English at Key Stage 3; a chart mapping the Objectives – and the activities that cover them – can be found at the beginning of each Activity section.

Many schools will simply read through the play in class with no staging at all, and the Activity sections have been written with this in mind, with individual activities ranging from debates and designing campaign posters to writing extra scenes or converting parts of the original novels into playscript form.

For those of you, however, who do wish to take to the stage, each OXFORD *Playscript* also features 'A Note on Staging' – a section dedicated to suggesting ways of staging the play, as well as examining the props and sets you may wish to use.

Above all, we hope you will enjoy using OXFORD *Playscripts*, be it on the stage or in the classroom.

What the Author Says

Troy 24 is inspired by *The Iliad,* an epic poem written in ancient Greece around 2,800 years ago. The poem tells the story of just ten days' fighting during the Trojan War, which, according to legend, lasted ten years. *The Iliad* also manages to look backwards and forwards across the whole of those ten years so that, by the end, we're in no doubt as to what the final outcome will be. *Troy 24* dramatises one of those ten days – one of the most crucial in the whole war – when the heroes Achilles and Hector face each other in battle. It is the fight between these two that forms the dramatic climax of *The Iliad.*

The Iliad was written by someone called Homer. Apart from his name, nothing for certain is known about him, and even his name is not an actual name. In its ancient Greek form, *Omeros,* it means 'the hostage'. What is certain is that Homer didn't make up the story of the epic on his own. Tales and legends of the Trojan War had been in existence for several hundred years before Homer was writing, learned by heart and recited and sung by bards and poets who travelled around Greece and the Mediterranean.

Homer may have been one of these wandering poets. But he happened to live at a time when the art of writing had just been imported from the Middle East. An alphabet had been invented for the Greek language, and stories and poems could now be written down, rather than simply memorised. With his great skill as a writer, Homer was able to take several stories from the Trojan War and weave them together to form a dramatic and thrilling epic poem of great length and complexity.

When I came to reread *The Iliad,* in an English translation, what struck me was how modern the writing seemed. And how visual. It was almost like reading a film script. *The Iliad* creates its battle scenes in a highly visual way, comparable to the way film-makers use the camera: the poem pans across the battlefield to give us a panoramic view of the fighting, then suddenly zooms in to concentrate on two individual warriors. It cuts away suddenly to another scene, freezes the action to describe some detail of armour or weaponry, or gives us flashbacks to fill in some detail of character or incident. When we remember that the poem was created when writing had only recently been invented, Homer's achievement seems even more amazing. In a way, Homer was both inventing the art of writing, and showing the way for film-makers in our own time!

Although Homer can't have been present at the Trojan War – the real war, if it happened at all, took place at least four hundred years before he was born – the poem reads as if he was. It's like reading an eyewitness account, a report from the battlefield. That must have been the effect on Homer's audience when they heard the poem spoken or chanted aloud.

It was that immediacy I wanted to try and capture in my dramatisation. I wanted that sense of this being a war that wasn't happening in the ancient past, but here and now, in our own time. So I came up with the idea of setting the play in a television studio, and of showing the events of this one day of the war as they would perhaps be reported to us by a 24-hour news channel, devoted entirely to the reporting of this particular conflict. I could use this framework to tell the story of the war in a brief, concise way, and at the same time focus on its most dramatic moments and characters. I could also have some fun, I thought, looking at the way in which events and information are edited and shaped for public consumption by the media.

Troy 24 isn't a version of *The Iliad*. It isn't the full story of the Trojan War. It leaves much out, and also includes some material not found in Homer's epic. And one character, Thersites, although he appears in a minor role in *The Iliad*, actually stepped into my play out of one by Shakespeare. *Troy 24* is an attempt to capture, for a modern audience, the immediacy, drama, and yes, the excitement of war as it is depicted in the original poem. It also tries to convey the tragedy of conflict – which is as real to us now as it was to the people of Homer's own time.

David Calcutt

A Note on Staging

The play follows events over the course of a single day during the ninth year of the Trojan War. It is set in the television studio of a 24-hour news channel, and in locations on the battlefield and within the camps of the rival armies. Occasional flashbacks recall some key moments from the early years of the conflict.

To allow the action to shift fluidly between scenes in different locations, the main acting area on the stage should be left empty. Scenes from the war can be created easily with actors and simple props – you might prefer to stage the battle scenes with imaginary 'mimed' weapons and use only the minimum of props, such as chairs which can be carried on and off the stage.

Depending on the size of your cast, actors may play several different characters in the play (doubling). So that you don't have lots of complicated costume changes, keep the costumes very simple. You could choose to have all actors in the same basic costume with small additions or props to distinguish them: Greek and Trojan soldiers might wear different colour armbands, for example; Helen might have a flower in her hair.

At the back of the stage is a white screen or cloth onto which images can be projected. Backlighting this screen will also allow you to create dramatic shadows when actors appear behind it.

Above the main stage, or to one side, is a raised area: the television studio. A brightly coloured sign with the words 'Olympian Broadcasting Corporation' is suspended above the heads of the two presenters. At the start of the play, the desks and the sign are in darkness, with only the main acting area lit.

Characters

Presenters and Reporters

For Troy 24:

Phoebe	television presenters
Perses	
Professor Omeros	expert commentator on the Trojan War
Iris	weather presenter
Reporter 1	reporters from the battlefield
Reporter 2	
Announcer 1	station announcers
Announcer 2	
Trojan correspondent	on location in the city of Troy
The Boss	the powerful owner of Olympian Broadcasting

For other broadcasters:

Spartan reporter 1	reporting on the elopement of **Paris** and **Helen**
Spartan reporter 2	
Correspondent 1	
Correspondent 2	
Correspondent 3	at **Agamemnon's** press conference
Correspondent 4	
Correspondent 5	
Correspondent 6	

Greeks

Patroclus	a hero; cousin of **Achilles** and second-in-command
Achilles	invincible champion of the Greek army
Agamemnon	the Greek commander-in-chief; brother of **Menelaus**
Menelaus	King of Sparta; wronged husband of **Helen**; brother of **Agamemnon**
Nestor	
Ajax	warriors and leaders of the Greek forces
Diomedes	
Odysseus	

Thersites	an opportunistic soldier
Myrmidon 1	
Myrmidon 2	
Myrmidon 3	soldiers of **Achilles**
Myrmidon 4	
Myrmidon 5	
Greek 1	
Greek 2	
Greek 3	soldiers
Greek 4	
Greek 5	

Trojans

Hector	commander-in-chief of the Trojan army
Aeneas	
Sarpedon	
Euphemus	warriors and leaders of the Trojan forces
Acamas	
Paris	son of King Priam; lover of **Helen**
Trojan 1	
Trojan 2	
Trojan 3	soldiers
Trojan 4	
Trojan soldier	victim of **Achilles**

Others

Chryseis	priestess of Apollo; enslaved by **Achilles**
Helen	Helen of Troy; estranged wife of **Menelaus** and lover of **Paris**
Aethra	**Helen's** maidservant

*The battlefield beneath the walls of Troy, at the end of a bitter day's fighting. An armed warrior enters and walks to centre stage. It is **Patroclus** wearing **Achilles's** armour. His face is hidden by his helmet.*

Patroclus

[Shouting offstage] Trojans! Turn and fight! There's nowhere to run, nowhere to hide! It's all over. Say your prayers. You're going to die beneath the walls of your city. And when you're dead, I'm going to destroy that city, kill your wives, kill all your children. I'll set fire to it, burn it to the ground. There'll be nothing left but old bones, cold ashes, broken stones. Troy will be no more!

Reporter 1 enters to one side of the stage.

Reporter 1

[To audience] I'm standing here beneath the walls of Troy, at a decisive moment in this long and bitter war. After an absence of ten days Achilles, the Greek champion, has returned to battle, causing panic among the Trojan troops. In a swift and savage attack, he has driven them back across the plain, and

now, in the shadow of the city, he brings his forces to a halt, to face the cowed* and broken army of Troy.

Patroclus *[Shouting offstage]* Are you all cowards? Will you die cowering in the dust like dogs, or will you die fighting, in the sunlight, like men? I'll give you a chance! Come forward one at a time! Face me in single combat! Who's first? No one? Is there no Trojan brave enough to face the sword of Achilles?

Hector enters in full armour.

Hector I'll fight you.

Reporter 1 But now, in yet another dramatic turn of events, Achilles's challenge has been taken up by Hector, the Trojan commander. And it seems now that all will be decided by single combat between these two champions.

Patroclus and Hector face each other.

Patroclus Hector.

Hector Achilles.

Patroclus You take my challenge?

Hector I do.

Patroclus So you're ready to die.

Hector As ready as you are.

Patroclus Here and now?

Hector Here and now.

Patroclus No more words, then.

Hector Let's fight.

Hector and Patroclus separate, to perform private rituals in honour of the gods.

Reporter 1 As they prepare for combat, a stillness has fallen across the battlefield. All eyes are fixed on these two mighty warriors,

* cowed – depressed or dispirited through fear

whose actions today will determine the outcome of the war. Each man dedicates himself to his gods, taking a handful of earth and sprinkling it over his head, as an acknowledgement of his own mortality.

Patroclus With this earth I salute you, gods of sky and sea.

Hector With this earth I offer my life, gods of air and light.

Patroclus You are sea, you are sky, I am as this earth.

Hector You are light, you are air, I am this dry earth.

Patroclus You are deathless, I am doomed to die.

Hector You are immortal, I shall not live forever.

Hector and Patroclus take up positions and draw their weapons. The fight begins.

Reporter 1 *[Commenting at moments during the fight]* It's evenly matched ... both looking for an opening, then going in for the attack ... And Hector appears to be the stronger ... Hector is definitely taking the advantage ... driving Achilles back with a series of blows ... relentless ... blow upon blow ... Achilles staggers ... and he's down ... Achilles is down.

Patroclus drops his sword and falls to his knees. Hector stands above him.

Hector Now are you ready to die?

Patroclus Strike, and strike fast.

Hector First take off your helmet. I wish to look Achilles in the face before I kill him.

Patroclus takes off his helmet. Hector reacts with shocked surprise.

Reporter 1 It's not Achilles! In a day of surprises, this has turned out to be the biggest surprise of all. The man we all thought was Achilles turns out to be his cousin and second-in-command, wearing Achilles's distinctive armour.

Hector	Patroclus!
Reporter 1	I repeat, this is *not* Achilles! The man about to die is Patroclus.

Hector rounds angrily on the reporter.

Hector	And he'll die with dignity! Turn your camera off!

Reporter 1 nods to Hector.

Reporter 1	*[To audience]* And with that dramatic revelation, it's back to the studio.

*Hector raises his sword to strike **Patroclus**. Blackout.*

• •

SCENE 2

*The television studio. Lights come up on the raised area, where **Perses** and **Phoebe** are seated at the two central desks.*

Phoebe	*[To audience]* This is *Troy 24* with exclusive footage of yesterday's remarkable turn of events in the battle for Troy.
Perses	Yesterday was certainly a day of surprises. First came the news that Achilles had apparently patched up his quarrel with the Greek commander-in-chief and taken up arms once more against the Trojans.

Phoebe	Then came the battle itself, with some of the most ferocious fighting we've seen in this war.
Perses	And finally, the revelation that the man leading the Greek forces was not Achilles, as we'd all thought, but his second-in-command, Patroclus.
Phoebe	As we saw in the footage, Patroclus died at the hands of Hector, before the two armies were forced to retire with the onset of night.
Perses	These events took place only yesterday, but *Troy 24* will be keeping you updated with events as they develop. We'll also be filling you in on the background to the dramatic occurrences of the last few days, and asking experts for their predictions on the future course of the war.
Phoebe	But first, let's return to more recent events, and in particular the death of Patroclus. As you know, Patroclus was not only Achilles's second-in-command, but also his closest friend. His death may well have a decisive impact, not least on the man responsible for his death, Prince Hector, the Trojan commander.
Perses	Our correspondent in Troy managed to obtain a brief interview with Prince Hector outside the city gates.

· ·

SCENE 3

*A spotlight comes up on **Hector**, standing centre stage. **Phoebe** and **Perses** observe from their studio seats.*

| Hector | [*To audience*] It came as a real shock to me. Like everybody else I thought it was Achilles. Then when he took his helmet off and I saw his face – well, after the initial shock I felt . . . disappointed. In Achilles. I'd always thought he was above that kind of thing. I thought he had more honour. |

*A spotlight shows **Patroclus** as we saw him last, kneeling with his head bowed, helmet off.*

And in a way, I felt sorry for Patroclus. Admired him too. He'd cut through our ranks, brought his men all the way to the city wall. It takes nerve to do that. And real fighting spirit. But he'd come too far, he was out of his depth. All he could do now was die, and he knew it. But before he died, he said something to me.

Patroclus [*As if to Hector*] It's not you that's killed me, Hector. It's fate. Fate tripped me, knocked me down. And fate's coming for you. You won't live long. I see death on your back.

Hector It was a brave thing to say. I could have spared him. But he was a Greek, and he had to die. I made it quick.

Light goes out on Patroclus.

I know that Achilles will come looking for me now. He and Patroclus were close. Everybody knows that. So it won't be long. Then we'll face each other in the field, and decide the outcome of this war once and for all.

Light goes out on Hector.

• •

SCENE 4

The television studio.

Phoebe Prince Hector speaking in an interview given just a few hours ago to our Trojan correspondent.

Perses Clearly, Hector now expects Achilles to return to the war. And if that proves to be the case, it could mark an end to the recent series of Trojan victories. It's been nine days since Achilles withdrew from the fighting and during that time the Greeks have suffered a series of terrible setbacks.

Phoebe We've seen them routed in the field by the Trojan forces . . .

Perses . . . driven back to their encampment by the sea . . .

Phoebe . . . their defences breached, their ships burned.

Perses But in all that time, Achilles has remained apart, refusing all entreaties⋆ by the various Greek commanders to save them from disaster.

⋆ entreaties – negotiations of peace

Phoebe	But will Patroclus's death now bring Achilles back to the war?
Perses	The only person who can answer that is Achilles himself. The Greek champion famously never gives interviews, and, since his withdrawal from the war, has refused the media access to his camp.
Phoebe	Despite this, one of our film crews did manage earlier to film secretly inside Achilles's camp, not long after Patroclus's body was brought back from the field.
Perses	This footage, which we're bringing you now, was filmed under difficult circumstances, and with no small danger to the crew.

• •

SCENE 5

*Achilles's camp. A group of his warriors – the **Myrmidons** – enter carrying **Patroclus's** body on a bier, covered in a cloth. **Achilles** enters.*

Achilles	Set it down there.
	They set the bier down.
	Did you have hard fighting?
Myrmidon 1	Every step of the way.
Myrmidon 2	They didn't want to give him up.
Achilles	He was a prize worth keeping.
Myrmidon 3	But we were determined to bring him back.
Myrmidon 4	We weren't going to let him fall into their hands.
Myrmidon 5	And there were more than a few of them paid for his killing.
Achilles	You're good men, all of you.
Myrmidon 1	We're *your* men, captain.
Myrmidon 2	Myrmidons.

Myrmidon 4	The best of the best.
Achilles	I know it.
	He steps up to the bier. ✱
	Pull back the cloth. Let me see him.
	*One **Myrmidon** draws back the cloth. **Achilles** steps closer, kneels beside the body. A spasm of emotion runs through his body. He reaches out to touch his face, but draws his hand back. Pause.*

Achilles	*[With tightness in his voice]* Did he make a good death?
Myrmidon 4	He died fighting like a man.
Myrmidon 5	A man, and a warrior.
	***Achilles** rises.*
Achilles	*[With mounting anger]* But he should not have died! Not today. Not yet. It was not his time. If he'd heeded my words he'd be living now. Drive the Trojans back from our ships, I said. Drive them back, then return. Leave Troy for another day, and for me. You all heard those words. Yet you all went on. Your blood was up, the taste of victory in your mouths. You had them on the run, and you followed him, all the way to

✱ bier – movable stand onto which a dead body is placed before burial

Troy, all the way to his death! And now you bring him back here – like this! And you haven't even wiped the blood from his face!

Myrmidon 1   We didn't think –

Myrmidon 2   There wasn't time.

Myrmidon 3   We brought him straight back.

Myrmidon 4   We thought you'd want to see him.

Myrmidon 5   I'll fetch some water.

Achilles   No! Leave him! Let the blood remain. I've been away too long. I'd almost forgotten it. Blood. It's why we're here. For blood. Blood and death. He took my death, died in my place. Now his blood speaks to me, it cries out, it calls for vengeance. And he shall have it! Hector killed him. So Hector will die. A Trojan killed him. Trojans will die. We'll wash my friend's body in Trojan blood. His funeral music will be the death screams of Trojans. From now on every Trojan is Hector. From now on every Trojan's a dead man. Troy is a city of corpses, a city of ghosts. Their children will not grow up. Their babies will not be born. Why did we come here to Troy?

Myrmidon 1   For glory!

Myrmidon 2   For honour!

Myrmidon 3   For fame!

Myrmidon 4   For blood!

Myrmidon 5   We came to kill Trojans!

Achilles   Yes. And now we are here for something else too. We're here for vengeance. Vengeance for the death of Patroclus. And tomorrow we'll take it. Tomorrow we'll win glory, honour, fame. Tomorrow, we feed on Trojans!

The Myrmidons cheer.

Take him. Lay his body beside my tent. He'll have his funeral when Hector's dead.

*The **Myrmidons** carry **Patroclus's** body on its bier offstage.*
__Achilles__ watches it go.

[To audience] Tomorrow we feed on Trojans.

He exits.

● ●

SCENE 6

The television studio.

Phoebe	Well, that does seem to confirm that Achilles will be returning to battle.
Perses	So tomorrow we may well see a change in the fortunes of the Greek forces.
Phoebe	But whatever the outcome, we'll certainly be seeing some more in the way of action.
Perses	And you can be sure that *Troy 24* will be on hand to bring you live coverage of that action.
Phoebe	But before that, coming up through the night, we'll be examining the background to Achilles's decision to withdraw from the war . . .
Perses	. . . and hearing from our correspondent inside the city of Troy, who, we hope, will bring us an exclusive interview with Helen of Troy herself.
Perses	Looking forward to that. There'll also be live updates from both the Greek and Trojan camps . . .
Phoebe	. . . as well as edited highlights of the whole progress of the war so far.
Perses	All that's to come on *Troy 24*.

Brash music: the Troy 24 theme tune. Two announcers enter.

Announcer 1	You're watching *Troy 24*.
Announcer 2	The only non-stop rolling news channel to bring you exclusive coverage of the Trojan War.

19

Announcer 1	All the action of the battlefield brought straight to your homes, 24 hours a day, seven days a week.
Announcer 2	*Troy 24* from Olympian Broadcasting.
Announcers	*[Together] Troy 24* – the war zone.

They exit, as the music ends. During their routine, Professor **Omeros** *has joined* **Phoebe** *and* **Perses** *in the studio.*

Perses	Yesterday's events came about as a direct result of the decision made by Achilles ten days ago, to withdraw from the war.
Phoebe	We're now going to look at the reasons behind his decision, and its consequences.
Perses	And to help us do that, we're joined in the studio by our expert commentator on the war, Professor Omeros.
Phoebe	Professor, perhaps you could take us back to the beginning of this chain of events.
Omeros	Certainly. The reason Achilles withdrew from the fighting was because of a quarrel between him and the Greek commander-in-chief.
Perses	Lord Agamemnon.
Omeros	But to discover the causes of that quarrel, we have to go back to the time when an epidemic of plague broke out among the Greek troops. This was at first put down to poor sanitary conditions, but many people believed that the plague was a result of direct divine intervention.
Perses	In other words, the plague was sent by a god.
Omeros	Yes. The god Apollo, to be precise. Whom Agamemnon had angered.
Phoebe	We have an extract of a filmed interview that illustrates that, Professor.
Perses	Here it is.

Spotlight on **Chryseis**, *centre stage.*

Chryseis	You think this plague comes from nature. You think it will be cured with medicines. You are wrong. It comes because of me. I am Chryseis, from the island of Lesvos. Greeks came to our island, led by Achilles. They raided our towns, took captives, I among them. I, Chryseis, priestess of Apollo. I was made slave to Agamemnon. My father came to Agamemnon, begged for my return. Agamemnon refused, beat my father. So my father prayed to Apollo. He called down a curse upon the Greeks. Let them suffer, he said. Fling down your arrows of disease and death. So the arrows fell, so the plague struck, so the Greeks died. My father came again to Agamemnon. This time Agamemnon let me go. Now the plague will end, when my feet tread the earth of my homeland. When I give thanks to Apollo. Let them take warning from this. Let all take warning.
	*Light fades on **Chryseis**.*
Omeros	Whether *we* believe it or not, it is a fact that the epidemic did end shortly after she left. And it was because Agamemnon had to send Chryseis back to her father that the now infamous quarrel between him and Achilles arose.
Perses	The first we knew about that was during a press conference Agamemnon gave shortly after the end of the epidemic.
Phoebe	We'll take a look at that now.

● ●

SCENE 7

	*The press conference. **Agamemnon** enters, accompanied by **Nestor**. **Press correspondents** enter from both sides of the stage.*
Nestor	*[To the correspondents]* Ladies and gentlemen, thank you for coming at such short notice. The commander-in-chief wishes to make a brief statement. After this, he will take a few questions. *[To **Agamemnon**]* Lord Agamemnon.
Agamemnon	Thank you, Nestor. *[He reads his statement]* As you know, in recent weeks the Greek forces have been severely disabled by an outbreak of plague. I'm happy to report that this has now been completely eradicated. It is time to once more turn our

attention to the job in hand. Therefore, at a meeting this morning of all the commanders of the Greek forces, it was decided to launch a major offensive against Troy. This will commence at first light tomorrow. Its aim will be the surrender and destruction of the city, and an end to this war. *[He has finished reading]* I will now take one or two short questions.

Correspondent 1	How long do you think it will take you to break through into Troy?
Agamemnon	We intend to be in by nightfall.
Correspondent 2	Do you expect heavy losses?
Agamemnon	There are always losses in war. But we expect the Trojans' losses will be greater than ours.
Correspondent 3	How certain are you of success?
Agamemnon	Completely. Otherwise we wouldn't launch it.
Nestor	*[Interjecting]* Just one more question.
Correspondent 4	Is it true that Achilles won't be taking part in this attack? There have been rumours –
Agamemnon	Achilles will not be taking part in the offensive.
Correspondent 5	Does that include his troops?
Nestor	*[Trying to close the press conference]* Please –
Agamemnon	*[To **Nestor**]* It's all right. *[To **correspondents**]* Neither Achilles nor his troops will be involved in tomorrow's operation.
Correspondent 6	Is that strategic planning? Or is it the case that you and Achilles have quarrelled –
Nestor	No more questions.
Correspondent 6	– and that he has in fact refused to play any further part in the war?

The **correspondents** shout their questions as **Nestor** holds up his hands.

Correspondent 1	What was the quarrel about?
Correspondent 2	Your tactics?
Correspondent 3	Your leadership?
Correspondent 4	The recent plague?
Correspondent 5	What will you do if he sails back home?
Correspondent 6	How can you win without Achilles?
Nestor	I'm sorry. Lord Agamemnon can't answer any more questions. Please leave now. We're very busy. There are preparations to be made.

Achilles enters, accompanied by Patroclus.

Achilles	Why don't you tell them? Answer their questions. Tell them the truth.
Agamemnon	What are you doing here? *[To Nestor]* How did he get past the guards?
Nestor	I don't know.
Achilles	Do you really think your men would dare to stand in my way?
Nestor	Achilles, I don't think this is the time –
Achilles	Yes, it is. It's just the time. Time to let the world know what kind of man it is that's running this war!
Nestor	Patroclus, speak to him.
Patroclus	I have. But you know what he's like ...
Achilles	Greedy, grasping, shameless ...
Patroclus	... once his mind's fixed ...
Achilles	... small-minded, mean-spirited ...
Patroclus	... there's no changing it.
Achilles	... strutting, swaggering, big-mouthed idiot!
Agamemnon	You dare speak to me like that!

Achilles	I speak the truth, that's all. And if it's not pleasant –
Agamemnon	If any other man said those things –
Achilles	But I'm not any other man. I'm Achilles!
Agamemnon	And I am Agamemnon! Your king and commander!
Achilles	King and commander! You? You're nothing more than a thief! You stole from me, took my property –
Agamemnon	A slave girl.
Achilles	*My* slave girl!
Agamemnon	She went back to her father. For the common good.
Achilles	When did you ever think of the common good! Only ever yourself, your own pride –
Nestor	It was his right.
Achilles	His right! To take what doesn't belong to him! Take, from me, from Achilles!
Agamemnon	And who is Achilles? Eh? What are you? A warrior, that's all. Here under my command!
Achilles	Your command! The great king! You fart and we all jump to attention.
Agamemnon	*[In a rage]* That's enough!
	*He raises his hand to strike **Achilles**.*
Achilles	Strike me and you're dead!
	***Achilles** puts his hand to his sword.*
Patroclus	Achilles! No!
	*He grabs **Achilles's** arm.*
Nestor	Agamemnon! Remember where we are! The press!
	*For a moment **Achilles** and **Agamemnon** face each other. Then **Achilles** relaxes, takes his hand off his sword.*

Achilles	All right! All right, Patroclus. He's not worth it. But he'll soon know what *I'm* worth. When the Trojans are on his tail. When he can smell his ships burning. He'll come to me then. On his knees. Begging for help. And he won't get it.

*Achilles turns and goes, followed by **Patroclus**. **Agamemnon** stares after them. **Nestor** turns to the correspondents.*

Nestor	Ladies and gentlemen, the press conference is over!

*Nestor hustles **Agamemnon** offstage. The **correspondents** exit, talking softly amongst themselves.*

• •

SCENE 8

The television studio.

Phoebe	Professor Omeros, perhaps you can talk us through what happened next.
Omeros	Certainly. The attack led by Agamemnon – without Achilles and his troops – was of course a failure. But that failure turned into near disaster for the Greeks, and, to understand why that was, we need to look closely at the position of the Greek forces – which we can do with this map.

A large map of the Greek camp is projected onto the screen.

Now, here to the far left of the map we have the coastline of the Trojan peninsula. The Greek contingents⋆ have their ships drawn up all along this coastline, and each contingent has its own camp erected around its ships. Way over to the right here is the city of Troy. And between themselves and Troy, the Greeks have built a massive defensive stockade which runs all the way from Agamemnon's camp, here at the top, to Achilles's camp, down here at the bottom. And in front of the stockade there's a trench, lined with sticks, and a wall built with packed earth from the trench. There's only one way in and out of these defences: a pathway that runs through the wall, across the trench and into the stockade by a gate – all of course heavily guarded.

⋆ contingents – troops forming part of an army

Perses	That would seem to be fairly impregnable, Professor.
Omeros	So it was – until Agamemnon launched his offensive. Because not only did the Greeks fail to take Troy, the Trojans launched their own counter-attack, completely routing the Greeks, and pushing them all the way back to the stockade. And that's when disaster struck.
Phoebe	As we'll see now in this extract of filmed report and interviews.

• •

SCENE 9

The battlefield in front of the Greek encampment. **Greek soldiers,** *with* **Thersites** *among them, run onstage in a panic.*

Greek 1	Fall back!
Greek 2	Run for it!
Greek 3	To the stockade!
Greek 4	Get inside!
Greek 5	Every man for himself!

Reporter 1 appears at the side of the stage.

Reporter 1	Here at the Greek stockade the scene is one of utter panic and confusion. Everywhere you look Greek soldiers are retreating in complete disorder, trying to make their way back inside the stockade before the Trojans arrive.

Reporter 1 retreats a safe distance upstage.

Thersites	What did I tell you? Didn't I say this attack was a mistake? Our leaders don't know what they're doing. If we stay here any longer we'll be food for worms.
Greek 1	He's right.
Greek 2	They've bungled the whole thing.
Greek 3	What do you say we should do, Thersites?
Thersites	What I said before. It's time to look out for ourselves. This

	isn't our war, it's theirs, our numbskull lords and masters. So let them fight it. The rest of us, back inside, get to the ships, and sail back home.
Greek 4	He's right! Back to the ships!
Greek 5	Let's go home!
	*They are about to exit when **Odysseus** enters.*
Greek 1	Lord Odysseus.
Odysseus	Stay where you are! Stand fast, and fight!
Thersites	Stand fast and die.
Odysseus	Thersites. Causing trouble again.
Thersites	I was just saying –
Odysseus	Too much! You're always saying too much. Words come spilling out of your mouth like a sewer pipe. *[He grabs **Thersites** by the scruff of his neck]* You try and stir up any more trouble with that foul mouth of yours, and I'll leave you here begging the Trojans to finish you off. Do you hear what I'm saying?
	*Ajax and **Diomedes** enter, followed by **Menelaus** supporting his wounded brother, **Agamemnon**.*
Ajax	Odysseus!
	***Odysseus** lets go of **Thersites**, who scarpers.*
Diomedes	Get inside the stockade!
Ajax	Agamemnon's wounded.
Menelaus	You men, help Lord Agamemnon. Take him to his tent.
	*Two soldiers come forward to help **Agamemnon**.*
Agamemnon	*[To **Menelaus**]* I was wrong, brother. I thought Zeus was with us, but he's abandoned us to the Trojans. *[To all]* Inside the stockade, all of you! Shut the gates fast! That's an order!
	*The soldiers help **Agamemnon** off stage.*

Odysseus	Menelaus. You're wounded yourself.
Menelaus	Show me a man who isn't.
Ajax	Hector's like a fury. He's everywhere at once.
Diomedes	There's a god fighting with him.
Menelaus	I had him – flung my spear – its aim was true. It would have struck him, but it swerved aside. Then there was a light – I was blinded – and he struck . . .

Menelaus staggers, almost falls.

Odysseus	*[To two of the soldiers]* You! Help Lord Menelaus. Take him inside.

The soldiers help Menelaus off stage.

Ajax	You too, Odysseus. Gather our people together. Prepare to defend the ships.
Diomedes	Ajax and I will hold them off as long as we can.
Odysseus	The ships? Once the gates are shut Hector can't break through.
Ajax	I think Hector can do anything he wants today.
Diomedes	Hurry! They're almost here!

Odysseus goes off stage. Reporter 1 comes forward.

Reporter 1	*[To audience]* And now the Trojan forces have come into sight, rushing forwards across the plain, crushing all that stands in their way. And the advance guard★ is already here, sweeping over the defences, across the bridge, and towards the gates of the stockade!

Reporter 1 retreats upstage. Trojan soldiers run on stage yelling. They are confronted by Ajax and Diomedes.

Ajax	Hold it there!
Diomedes	Not a step further!

★ advance guard – the forward division in an army

Trojan 1	Ajax!
Trojan 2	Diomedes!
Ajax	The first to come forward's a dead man!
Diomedes	So. Who's it going to be?

*The **Trojans** stand their ground, but uneasily.*

Ajax	*[To a soldier]* You?
Diomedes	*[To another soldier]* Or you?
Ajax	Come on! Make your minds up!
Diomedes	Or all of you at once?

*Ajax and **Diomedes** take a step forward, weapons raised, shouting. The **Trojans** turn and flee.*

Ajax	They'll be back.
Diomedes	And soon.
Ajax	And next time with Hector.

*Ajax and **Diomedes** exit upstage. **Reporter 1** reappears.*

Reporter 1	The Greeks have retreated into their stockade, its heavy gates shut fast. But will they be strong enough to stop Hector? We won't have to wait long to find out. I can see the main body of the Trojan force now, storming over the ramparts, with Prince Hector leading them.

*Reporter 1 moves upstage again as **Hector** enters, accompanied by **Aeneas** and **Sarpedon**.*

Aeneas	The gates are shut.
Sarpedon	With the Greeks behind them, cowering like dogs.
Aeneas	Not like dogs, Sarpedon. Like wolves, waiting to tear our throats.
Sarpedon	Then we should leave them there to howl.
Hector	Leave them, Sarpedon? Have we come so far only to turn back

and go home to Troy? No. God's strong with us today. I feel his power in me. He means us to go on.

Aeneas	Through the gates?
Hector	Through the gates, Aeneas.
Sarpedon	And then?
Hector	Then we'll slaughter these Greeks among their own tents, burn their ships, and leave their bodies to the sea. Gather our troops, prepare them for battle. This war's gone on too long. It ends now, and it ends here.

Ajax and Sarpedon exit. Hector kneels, bows his head in prayer, takes a handful of earth, raises it to the sky, then smears it on his face. Trojan soldiers enter. Hector rises to his feet.

Hector	*[A war cry]* Death to the Greeks!
Trojans	Death to the Greeks!

Greek soldiers, led by Ajax and Diomedes, enter from the other side.

Greeks	Death to the Trojans!

*Greek and Trojan soldiers advance on each other. There follows a series of still images of fighting. **Aeneas, Sarpedon, Ajax** and **Diomedes** speak to the audience, as in interviews given later. Soldiers move from one still image to another between speeches.*

Aeneas	It was all down to Hector. We'd have followed him anywhere. He led us in the charge and we smashed through the gates.
Sarpedon	They were waiting for us, and there was some hard fighting. A lot of us died there. A lot of them did as well.

Still image.

Ajax	We held them off for as long as we could. But there were too many of them and they just kept coming.
Diomedes	It was chaos. There was nobody there to give orders, and every man just had to fight for himself.

Still image.

Aeneas	They had us hemmed in by the gate, and it looked like we weren't going to be able to break through. At one point they even started to push us back. Then I saw Hector.
Sarpedon	He raised his spear and gave a cry, then plunged straight into the enemy. That put heart into us. We followed, and the Greeks broke and ran.

Still image.

Ajax	Hector was cutting his way through our troops, and his men were following. There was nothing else we could do. We gave the order to fall back.
Diomedes	They came after us, and we knew what it was they wanted. So we took up positions around the ships, and made ready to fight and hold them off.

Still image.

Aeneas	So there we were at last. We'd pushed them right back, and all we had to do was finish them off.
Sarpedon	And being right there in their camp, and seeing their ships in front of us, we were sure this was going to be victory.

Still image.

| Ajax | We fought hard, we held our ground. And we knew that if we could hold them off till dark we'd be all right. |

| Diomedes | Then I smelled smoke and looked up and saw the ships on fire. And I thought, this is it, we're done for, it's finished. |

A final still image.

● ●

SCENE 10

The television studio.

| Omeros | And so it would have been, had it not been for Patroclus's timely intervention. Mistaking him for Achilles – the one man they all feared – the Trojan forces quickly retreated with Patroclus in pursuit, thus bringing about a complete, and timely reversal of Greek fortunes. |

| Perses | Which brings us to how things stand at present. |

| Omeros | Indeed. |

| Perses | Well, thank you for that, Professor. We look forward to hearing from you again later. |

| Omeros | Thank you. |

Professor Omeros exits.

| Phoebe | Now, some breaking news. *Troy 24* has been sent a remarkable piece of film. Shot secretly early yesterday morning in Achilles's camp, it apparently shows the circumstances that led to Patroclus's dramatic, and doomed, intervention in the war. |

| Perses | The film, from an unnamed source, also gives a revealing insight into the character of Achilles. |

| Phoebe | Very up close and personal. And something of a *Troy 24* exclusive, isn't it? |

| Perses | It certainly is. And I think – yes we are – we're ready to look at that film now. |

| Phoebe | Here it is. |

SCENE 11

*Achilles's tent. **Patroclus** and **Achilles** are arguing.*

Patroclus	They've broken through the defences. They've reached the ships.
Achilles	Whose ships?
Patroclus	Nestor's.
Achilles	They're a long way from ours.
Patroclus	Some are on fire – *burning*. . .
Achilles	He can afford to lose a few.
Patroclus	Agamemnon's wounded, and Diomedes, and Odysseus.
Achilles	It goes with the job.
Patroclus	Hundreds of Greeks lie dead on the shore!
Achilles	This is war.
Patroclus	And we're losing it. Because you won't fight.
Achilles	We? This isn't my war. I didn't lose my wife to a Trojan glamour boy, like Menelaus. I swore no allegiance to Agamemnon.
Patroclus	But you came. You came because you chose to.
Achilles	Exactly. And now I choose not to fight.
Patroclus	Because of a slave girl.
Achilles	Because of my honour! Because he insulted me! My honour's all I have. He took it. I want it back. I want him wounded and weeping and begging, here!
Patroclus	He'll never do that.
Achilles	Then Greeks will die.
Patroclus	And we'll sail back and live a long and happy life.
Achilles	You know we won't. A long and happy life . . . I gave that up

to fight at Troy. I'll never see my home again. My bones will lie here. I chose that fate, and I deserve some respect for it.

Patroclus	I know. But who will there be left alive to give you that respect, unless you stop Hector now?
Achilles	I can't.
Patroclus	Then let me.
Achilles	You?
Patroclus	I'll go into battle, lead your troops. And if I wear your armour –
Achilles	What?
Patroclus	The Trojans will think I'm you. They won't dare attack. I'll drive them from the ships – and then take Troy.
Achilles	No. Once the beach is clear, come back. The ships will be safe, we'll have a breathing space –
Patroclus	Stop. Quiet.
Achilles	What is it?
Patroclus	I heard something. Outside the tent. There might be someone there. One of those reporters after a story. Take a look.

Sudden blackout, as if the filming was interrupted.

• •

SCENE 12

The television studio.

Phoebe	So, there we have it. The full story behind Patroclus's dramatic action yesterday.
Perses	An action which drove the Trojans back from the Greek ships, and saved the Greeks from disaster – and has now brought Achilles back to the war.
Phoebe	With Achilles vowing to take vengeance on Hector, what will happen when these two champions meet?

Perses	It seems certain only one will survive that encounter. And whoever does will determine the outcome of the war.
Phoebe	*Troy 24* will be there as always to bring you live-action coverage of that battle as it takes place.
Perses	And while that's still some time off, this is a good time to take a look back at the key events of the war, and to remind ourselves what it was that set these two great powers in conflict with each other.
Phoebe	There'll be that, and a lot more, after a short break.
Perses	We'll leave you with that footage of Achilles making the historic declaration of his return to the war.

*Spotlight on **Achilles**, centre stage.*

Achilles	Hector killed him. So Hector will die. A Trojan killed him. Trojans will die. We'll wash my friend's body in Trojan blood. His funeral music will be the death screams of Trojans. From now on every Trojan is Hector. From now on every Trojan's a dead man.

*Light goes out on **Achilles**. Music: Troy 24 theme tune. **Phoebe** and **Perses** relax, off air.*

Perses	So, who's your money on?
Phoebe	Between Achilles and Hector? Achilles. What about you?
Perses	I think it's pretty even. Could go either way.
Phoebe	No. It's got to be Achilles.
Perses	Hector's good.
Phoebe	He's good, but he's not great. Achilles is great. Hector's no match for him.
Perses	I'm not so sure.

***Thersites** enters.*

Thersites	Hello.

Perses and Phoebe look at him, surprised.

Phoebe	Who are you?
Perses	What are you doing here?
Thersites	He said I could have a look around.
Perses	Who did?
Thersites	Whatsisname. Him that puts it all together. The show.
Phoebe	The producer?
Thersites	That's him, yes. The producer.
Perses	I don't think so. We don't have visitors in the studio.
Thersites	Ask him if you like.
Phoebe	*[To Perses]* Give him a call.

Perses picks up the phone.

Perses	Give me the control room, will you? Thanks.

Perses talks on the phone. Thersites comes closer.

Thersites	So this is where it all comes from, is it?
Phoebe	You've been told you can't come in here.
Thersites	That's where you're wrong. You'll find out in a minute. *[Looking around]* Very nice, isn't it? Very plush. Not much like our tents. You've got it all right, you have.
Phoebe	Look, just who are you?

Perses puts down the phone.

Perses	*[To Phoebe]* He's the unnamed source.
Phoebe	What?
Perses	The one who shot the film we've just shown.
Phoebe	Him?
Perses	Yes.

Phoebe	And he has permission?
Perses	Yes.
Thersites	Told you, didn't I? I came to bring the film. And the producer, he said, 'Why don't you stay and watch it go out?' So I did. Very good, it was. You do a good job, you two.
Phoebe	*[Dryly]* Thanks.
Thersites	The producer said I could pop in and see you before I went back to camp. So here I am.
Perses	Here you are. Thersites. That's your name, isn't it? Thersites.
Thersites	Yes, but don't go letting on, will you? To your viewers, I mean. I've got to remain anonymous. For my own safety. If Achilles was to find out, I wouldn't be worth dog's meat.
Phoebe	You're a soldier, then.
Thersites	Rank and file, yes. Battle fodder. The sweepings of the street, that's what they call us.
Perses	Who?
Thersites	Them. Agamemnon, Menelaus, Ajax, Odysseus, Achilles. The kings and lords of Greece. The stars of your show. They don't have much time for us. Except when they want us to die for them.
Phoebe	Perhaps you'd like to give an interview. The war from the ordinary soldier's point of view.
Perses	We could do it now, when we go back on air. As you're here.
Thersites	No, thanks. It's more than my life's worth. I've got what I want out of you lot. And you got what you want out of me. So that's okay. You pay well, I'll give you that. Very generous. You must be doing well out of the war. I mean, look at it all! These studios. And I bet you two are doing all right.
Phoebe	That's none of your business.
Thersites	I'm not criticizing you. You got to grab what you can while

you got the chance. The war ain't going last forever, is it? And what happens then? We're all out of a job. That's why I took the film, why I sold it. I'm well set up now. No more soldiering for me after tomorrow. It's a mug's game.

Perses	So you will be fighting tomorrow?
Thersites	Oh, yes. I'll be there.
Perses	Why? You have that money. You don't need to fight.
Thersites	Got to, haven't I? Don't have much choice. If I take off now they'll miss me, bring me back. It'll be easier to get away once the battle's started. But don't worry, I know how to look after myself.
Perses	I'm sure you do.
Thersites	Well, then. I'd better be off. Thanks very much.
Phoebe	One more question before you go. How did you manage to get that film?
Thersites	I was lucky. Just happened to be by the tent. I saw Patroclus go running in. Just come down from where the Trojans were burning the ships. Looked all upset, he did. And as there wasn't nobody around. . .
Phoebe	I meant how did you get hold of a camera?
Thersites	The camera?
Phoebe	Yes. The film quality was very good.
Thersites	I found it.
Phoebe	Found it.
Thersites	On the battlefield.
Phoebe	Just lying around, was it?
Thersites	That's right. Another bit of luck, really. *[Turns to go, then stops]* Oh, and there was a body next to it. A cameraman. One of yours, I think.

Perses	One of ours?
Phoebe	Someone did go missing a few days ago.
Thersites	Looks like I found him.
Perses	And took his camera.
Thersites	Wasn't any more use to him, was it?
Perses	You didn't see who killed him.
Thersites	You don't see who kills who in the middle of a battle. Most of the time you don't know who you're killing, yourself. And if somebody who shouldn't be there gets in the way –
Phoebe	Are you saying –?
Thersites	He must've got a bit too close to the action. Dangerous line of work, isn't it? If you get in the way? Very dangerous. Not for you, though. You're safe and sound tucked away in here.

Troy 24 music fades in.

Sounds like you're going back on. Better be off. Thanks again. I'll see myself out.

Thersites *exits. The show is back on air. The two announcers enter to centre stage.*

Announcer 1	You're watching *Troy 24*.
Announcer 2	*Troy 24*, the battlefield channel.
Announcer 1	All the action, and the stories behind the action.
Announcer 2	All the issues, and the people behind the issues.
Announcer 1	If it's there to be seen, it's on your screen.
Announcer 2	*Troy 24* – the people's war.
	Announcers exit.
Phoebe	*[To audience]* Welcome back. As we wait for what may be the most decisive battle of the war, let's remind ourselves of the original causes of the conflict, and some of its key events and characters.
Perses	So stay with us as we take a look back with this specially compiled montage of the headlines, images, interviews and events that have held our attention over the past ten years.
Phoebe	Here's how it all began.

• •

SCENE 13

*Music. Lights dim on studio, though **Phoebe** and **Perses** remain visible. A headline appears on the screen:*

SCANDAL IN SPARTA

Spartan reporter 1 enters.

Sp. reporter 1	Scandal has rocked the Greek city of Sparta as it was revealed that Helen, wife to King Menelaus, has abandoned her husband and homeland to run away with Paris, younger son of King Priam of Troy.
	Spartan reporter 2 enters.
Sp. reporter 2	Paris was heading a state visit to Sparta with the intention of negotiating a trade agreement with Troy. And it was when Menelaus was suddenly called away on urgent business that the couple apparently took the opportunity to elope.

Sp. reporter 1	We don't yet know whether this was planned beforehand, or if it was a spur-of-the-moment decision.
Sp. reporter 2	Nor indeed how willing a partner Helen was or if, as those close to Menelaus are claiming, Paris abducted her against her will.
Sp. reporter 1	But whatever the truth, the affair is bound to have serious repercussions, not only for relations between Sparta and Troy but for the whole of Greece and the eastern Aegean.

The two reporters exit. A second headline appears on screen:

GIFT OF THE GODS – PARIS AND HELEN CONFESS THEIR LOVE

Paris and Helen enter.

Helen	*[To audience]* Took me by force? Menelaus would say that, wouldn't he? It would never occur to him that I might have a mind of my own, let alone feelings.
Paris	*[To audience]* It was love at first sight for both of us. I'd been told she was the most beautiful woman in the world, but I didn't realise what they meant until I saw her.
Helen	And Paris isn't half bad either. But, of course, there's a lot more to it than just physical attraction.
Paris	We were destined for each other. Quite literally. Aphrodite, the goddess of love, promised her to me.
Helen	He had a dream – didn't you?
Paris	A vision.
Helen	She appeared to him in this vision and told him that the most beautiful woman in the world would be his.
Paris	And that's Helen. A gift of the gods.
Helen	So really, neither of us are to blame. Once Aphrodite casts her spell on you there's nothing you can do about it.
Paris	And there's nothing Menelaus can do either. It's heaven's will. No mortal can oppose that.

Helen	I don't know why he's making such a fuss. We didn't marry for love, or anything like that. It was all arranged between him and my father. He didn't so much gain a wife as gain a city. Sparta. And he's welcome to it.
Paris	He has Sparta, Troy has Helen. That's fair. And I think we should leave it at that.

Paris and Helen exit. Menelaus enters as another headline appears on the screen:

MENELAUS VOWS VENGEANCE – 'IT'S WAR!' SAY GREEKS

Menelaus	*[To audience]* How do you think I damn well feel? He was my guest! He violated a most sacred trust! I welcomed him into my home, and this is how he repays me! It's more than an insult. It's an outrage!

Agamemnon enters.

Agamemnon	*[To audience]* An outrage against my brother, an outrage against me. An outrage against every city in Greece.
Menelaus	If he thinks he'll get away with it, he's got another thing coming.
Agamemnon	It's a deliberate act of provocation. And if Greece is provoked, Greece will respond.
Menelaus	It's not just Helen I want back, it's my pride. My reputation. I want reparations. I demand vengeance!
Agamemnon	All the Greek rulers have pledged their support.

Diomedes, Odysseus, Nestor and Ajax enter.

Diomedes	Diomedes of Argos.
Odysseus	Odysseus of Ithaca.
Nestor	Nestor of Pylos.
Ajax	Ajax of Salamis.
Agamemnon	Troops are gathering, a fleet is being assembled. With a good

wind, we'll set sail for Troy. And there we'll make our demands.

Diomedes	Return Helen.
Odysseus	Make reparations.
Nestor	If not, it's war.
Ajax	And if it's war, Greece will win.
Agamemnon	And if it's war, Troy will die.

A new headline appears on the screen:

TROY STANDS FIRM

Hector and Paris enter.

Hector We don't seek war with these Greeks. We're a peaceful people, and it's our hope that we can find a peaceful solution to this matter. But if one can't be found, if war comes, then we're ready for it. Our troops are fresh and fit for battle. And we have allies and friends who have answered our call for aid.

Aeneas, Sarpedon, Euphemus and Acamas enter.

Aeneas	Aeneas of Dardania.
Sarpedon	Sarpedon of Lycia.
Euphemus	Euphemus of Ciconia.
Acamas	Acamas of Thrace.
Paris	*[To audience]* Helen came here of her own free will. She's chosen Troy, and we'll defend her right to make that choice. Troy is a free city, a sovereign state. It will not subject itself to threat and force. And if Greece has demands to make of us, we have demands to make of Greece.
Aeneas	Turn back from our shores.
Sarpedon	Return to your homes.
Euphemus	Leave us in peace.

Acamas	Or Troy will fight.
Hector	And if Troy fights, Troy will prevail.

The two armies turn to face each other. A new headline appears on the screen:

ACHILLES JOINS GREEKS

Achilles enters.

Achilles	*[To audience]* Agamemnon asked me to fight for him in this war. 'Bring your Myrmidon troops,' he said. 'We need them. We need Achilles.' I told him, this is not my war. I don't care about Helen. I don't care about Troy. But I will fight. Not for you. For me. At my birth a prophecy was made. I was given two destinies: the first, to live a long, contented, peaceful life, to die at home, become dust, be forgotten; the second, to win fame and glory, die young in battle, my name remembered forever. This is what I have chosen. After death there is nothing but dust and shadows. All that remains are our names in other men's mouths. So I will fight and I will die at Troy. The name of Achilles will make this war famous, and will be spoken as long as men walk the earth.

Achilles exits. A final headline appears on the screen:

GREEK FORCES LAND AT TROY

Two reporters enter and stand on opposite sides of the stage.

Reporter 1	Out there on the ocean the Greek fleet approaches, and it truly is a breathtaking sight –
Reporter 2	Up there on the hill stands the city of Troy, magnificent, commanding the entire plain –
Reporter 1	– and as they approach the shore, men leap out into the shallows –
Reporter 2	– and from behind its walls a trumpet sounds its deep note –
Reporter 1	– drag their ships up onto the beach, and begin preparing themselves for battle –

Reporter 2	– and the great gate of Troy swings open, and the Trojan army, led by Hector, marches out –
Reporter 1	– Greeks advancing to the plain, taking up their positions –
Reporter 2	– Trojans moving down to the plain, taking up their positions –
Reporters 1 & 2	*[Speaking together]* – each troop assembled behind its commander.
Reporter 1	And though both sides appear ready for battle –
Reporter 2	Neither seems willing to make the first move –
Reporter 1	And all we can hear is the wind and the sea –
Reporter 2	As an eagle sweeps over the sun-baked plain.
	Hector steps forward.
Hector	Greeks! Why have you come armed to our shores? What quarrel do you have with us? Who speaks for you?
	Agamemnon steps forward.
Agamemnon	I do, Agamemnon of Mycenae. We're here to take back my brother's wife, stolen from him by your brother.
Paris	That's not true!
	Hector shoots a warning glance at Paris, who falls silent.
Hector	Go on.
Agamemnon	And for reparations.
Hector	Reparations?
Agamemnon	Compensation for the cost of this enterprise – and for my brother's damaged honour. I think that's fair.
Hector	That depends on the cost of those reparations.
Agamemnon	I'm sure we can work something out.
Hector	Perhaps we can.
Paris	You can work out what you like. But Helen stays here.

Hector	Paris –
Paris	I won't give her up.
Menelaus	She's my wife!
Paris	Not anymore.
Menelaus	You took her!
Paris	She came willingly.
Menelaus	Give her back.
Paris	She's staying here.
Menelaus	She belongs to me!
Paris	She belongs to *me!*
Menelaus	Trojan scum!
Paris	Greek trash!
Hector	That's enough!
Agamemnon	No more talking!
Hector	Prepare for battle!
Agamemnon	It's war!

The two reporters step forward.

Reporter 1	Then a cry rings out –
Reporter 2	Men's voices roar –
Reporter 1 & 2	*[Together]* – and the army charges across the plain!

The reporters exit. With a huge roar, Greeks and Trojans advance on each other, and freeze in an image of fighting. Fade to blackout.

SCENE 14

The television studio.

Phoebe   This is *Troy 24*. We've been looking at the original causes of this conflict.

Perses   A conflict that has dragged for nine gruelling years, but which now may well be approaching its end.

Phoebe   Or, if not the end, the beginning of the end.

Perses   And as we approach that end, it's time to turn our attention to the woman at the centre of the conflict: Helen of Sparta, now known as Helen of Troy.

Phoebe   Since her arrival in the city nine years ago, very little has been seen of her; and, though we've often asked, she's never consented to be interviewed for this programme.

Perses   Until now. Just a few hours ago she did at last agree to speak to our correspondent in Troy.

Phoebe   In an interview that many of you will find quite startling, it's clear that her nine years as a virtual prisoner in Troy have taken their toll.

Perses   Not least in her attitude towards Paris, and her adopted city.

Phoebe   As time is short, we're only going to show a brief clip, though we will be bringing you the full interview at a later date.

Perses   Here she is, then, speaking in her apartment in the royal citadel: Helen of Troy.

Helen's apartment. She is seated opposite the Trojan Correspondent, in mid interview.

Helen   I can't remember the last time I went out. I never leave the citadel, nor even my apartment. I'm more or less a prisoner here. They tell me it's for my own safety. Apparently, I'm no longer popular. There was a time when I was, when Paris first brought me here. They couldn't see enough of me then. I was a prize worth having. But not anymore. So I have to stay shut in here, and spend my days sewing or weaving like some village wife.

Correspondent   Why do you think that is, that you're no longer popular?

Helen   The war, of course. They blame me. Dog-faced Helen. That's what they call me, apparently. One of the things they call me. I'm the cause of all their woes and suffering.

Correspondent   And are you?

Helen   No. I'm as much a victim of this war as they are. I'm not to blame for it. If anyone's to blame it's Paris –

Aethra, Helen's servant, enters. She carries a robe over her arm.

Aethra	Madam –
Helen	What do you want? Can't you see I'm busy?
Aethra	You asked me to bring your robe.
Helen	Did I?
Correspondent	Yes, you did.
Helen	Oh. Very well, then.
Aethra	Shall I put it on you?
Helen	Not yet. In a moment. Just wait there. *[To the correspondent]* Excuse me. Please carry on.
Correspondent	You were talking about Paris.
Helen	Paris. Have you seen him lately? If you have it won't have been on the battlefield. He's let himself go. His looks certainly aren't what they were. And he has a belly. His whole body's just beginning to . . . sag. I was a fool to let him take me away from my home. He more or less forced me.
Correspondent	But you said when you first arrived that you'd come here willingly – because of your love for Paris.

Helen does not reply and simply looks at the correspondent for a moment. She turns to Aethra.

Helen	Aethra. I'll wear my robe now.
Aethra	Yes, madam.

Helen stands and waits as Aethra approaches her and begins to dress her in the robe, which has a large pin to fasten it.

Helen	Came willingly? I would say that then, wouldn't I? I was under his influence. I didn't really know what I was doing. I think he may have used some kind of drug. Or sorcery. Probably both. They do that kind of thing here in the east.

*Aethra accidentally pricks **Helen** with the pin. **Helen** snaps at her.*

Be careful!

Aethra	Sorry, madam –
Helen	That hurt. You've drawn blood!
Aethra	I am so sorry. I didn't mean to –
Helen	Yes, you did. You did it on purpose, you Trojan slut!

*She raises her hand to strike **Aethra**, who flinches away. **Helen's** hand stays poised to strike, then she lets it drop.*

[To **correspondent**] Forgive me ... that little outburst. It's my nerves: being cooped up here. Sometimes the strain is ... too much. Nine years. It feels more like nine hundred. I've grown to hate the place. Loathe it. And them. My in-laws. The First Family of Troy. The stories I could tell you about them! Oh, I can't wait for Menelaus to come and take me back to Sparta. And he will. These Trojans are no match for the Greeks. I know they have Hector, but the Greeks have Achilles, and he's fighting tomorrow. It won't be long. You'll see. Soon I'll be sailing back across the sea to Greece. And this whole beastly city will be burned to the ground.

*She turns to **Aethra,** holds out the robe.*

Take this. I don't think I shall wear it after all.

Aethra	Yes, madam.

Aethra takes the robe.

Helen	And Aethra. Please be a dear and bring us both something to drink.

*Aethra exits. **Helen** sits down.*

SCENE 16

The television studio.

Phoebe	So it seems that all's not happy in the Trojan royal household. And what Helen has to say certainly raises many questions.
Perses	Not the least being why it is that the Trojans are still allowing the war to continue. If she wants to return now to Greece, why don't they just let her?
Phoebe	Are they keeping her prisoner, as she maintains?
Perses	Is the war actually about Helen at all?
Phoebe	We'll be having an in-depth discussion about those, and other questions, later on. But for now, it's time to return to more pressing matters.
Perses	Although it's still night, in both the Greek and the Trojan camp preparations are underway for tomorrow's battle. So we're going to go live now to our news teams in the field to see what's happening there.
Phoebe	First, our correspondent in the Trojan camp.

SCENE 17

*The Trojan camp. **Reporter 2** is standing with a group of four Trojan soldiers.*

Reporter 2	I'm here in the Trojan camp, outside the walls of the city. And such is the size of the Trojan force that it resembles a small city in itself. Campfires are burning all over the hillside and the slopes leading down to the plain. And here, standing beside one of those campfires, are four ordinary Trojan soldiers, who have agreed to say a few words about the coming battle. *[Turning to the soldiers]* Everyone agrees that today's battle could be decisive. Are you all feeling confident?
Trojan 1	Very confident. We're in good shape. And keen to finish the job.

Reporter 2	By 'finish the job' you mean defeat the Greeks once and for all.
Trojan 2	Not just defeat them. Annihilate them.
Trojan 3	We've got them on the run now. We beat them all the way back to the beach.
Trojan 4	And burned their ships.
Reporter 2	That was until yesterday –
Trojan 1	Yesterday was a fluke. It won't happen again.
Trojan 2	That's right. Hector will see to that.
Trojan 4	Hector's the man. There's nothing we wouldn't do for him.

Hector enters.

| Trojan 1 | And I'll tell you what Hector's going to do for us – |
| Hector | Why don't you tell me as well? Then I can make sure I get it right. |

The soldiers all spring to attention.

| Trojan 1 | Lord Hector! |
| Hector | At ease, men. |

They stand at ease.

[To Trojan 1] Now, what was it you were saying I'm going to do for you?

Trojan 1	I didn't mean nothing by it, Lord Hector. Nothing disrespectful. I was just saying, you know –
Hector	It's all right, go on.
Trojan 1	Well, I was just going to say that tomorrow you're going to send them Greeks back where they come from.
Trojan 2	Them that are left alive.
Trojan 3	And there won't be many.

Trojan 4	This time tomorrow, there won't be a Greek left standing on Trojan earth.
Hector	Well, there's only one way I can do all that, and that's with your help.
Trojan 1	You'll have that all right, sir.
Trojan 2	You can count on us.
Trojan 3	We'll be with you all the way.
Trojan 4	Right down the line.
Hector	I never doubted it. And if we're going to beat them we'd best get ready for it. Sunrise isn't far off. About your duties, men.
Trojans	Yes, sir!
	The soldiers exit.
Reporter 2	Lord Hector. Can you spare a few moments?
Hector	A few, yes.
Reporter 2	Thank you. I just wanted to ask you, now that your men have gone, how confident are you really of victory tomorrow?
Hector	Absolutely certain. I have no doubt of it.
Reporter 2	You know by now that Achilles is returning to the field –
Hector	Achilles is a formidable opponent. I look forward to meeting him in combat. And to defeating him.
Reporter 2	What makes you so certain that you will?
Hector	I'll tell you. It's because we're fighting for something. Our homes, our families, our way of life, our freedom. This is our land, where we were born, and where our ancestors were born. We're rooted to it, it makes us strong, stronger than the Greeks. Troy, that's what we're fighting for, and that's why we'll win. Now, I have to go and prepare for that victory.
Reporter 2	Of course. Thank you, Lord Hector.
	Hector exits.

[To audience] So that's the mood here in the Trojan camp – one of resolution and complete confidence. It's the mood of Hector himself as he prepares for the conflict to come. But will that confidence be enough to carry him and the rest of the Trojan army through to victory? In a little while the sun will be rising, and battle will be joined. Then we'll know. Now, over to our correspondent in the Greek camp.

SCENE 18

The Greek camp. **Reporter 1** *enters from the other side of the stage.*

Reporter 1	I'm here on the outskirts of the Greek camp. Though it's still dark, I can hear from inside the stockade a huge amount of activity. I've been unable to get an interview with any of the Greek commanders, but I do know that they've been badly shaken by the success of the recent Trojan attack, and I think they're determined that –

Four **Greek soldiers** *enter.*

Greek 1	Who are you?
Greek 2	What are you doing here?
Greek 3	Where you from?
Greek 4	Friend or foe?
Reporter 1	I'm a correspondent with –
Greek 1	You a spy?
Greek 2	A Trojan spy.
Reporter 1	I'm not –
Greek 3	He's a spy.
Greek 4	We've got ourselves a Trojan spy!
Reporter 1	I've told you, I'm not a spy, or a Trojan. I'm a reporter from Olympian Broadcasting. You know us. We're covering the

war. *[Pointing towards the audience]* Look, there's the camera. You see?

The soldiers turn towards the audience.

Greek 1   He's right. There's a camera.

Greek 2   Filming us.

Greek 3   Filming our camp.

Greek 4   Spying on us.

Reporter 1   No –

They turn back to him.

Greek 1   It's just like we said.

Greek 2   You're a Trojan spy.

Greek 3   Making a secret film for the enemy.

Greek 4   You know what we do with spies?

Greek 1   We execute them.

Greek 2   Cut their throats.

Greek 3   Throw their bodies to the dogs.

Greek 4   And that's what we're going to do with you.

Greek 1   And your cameraman can film it.

Greek 2   In close-up.

Greek 3   Then give it to the Trojans. .

Greek 4   So they can see what happens to their spies.

The soldiers close in on the reporter.

Reporter 1   *[Pleading]* But I'm not a spy – please – you must believe me. *[To audience]* Don't just stand there – do something! Stop filming, they're going to kill me!

***Odysseus** enters.*

Odysseus	All right, boys. That's enough. Let him go. *[They release the reporter]* We've had our joke now.
Reporter 1	Your joke?
Odysseus	That's right. A little bit of fun. I'm Odysseus of Ithaca. These are my boys.
Reporter 1	Oh ... Odysseus.
Odysseus	They'll be going into battle soon. There's not much to laugh about out there. And some of them might not come back. It does them good to have a bit of a joke. Keeps their spirits up. You don't begrudge them that, do you?
Reporter 1	No, of course not.
Odysseus	*[To soldiers]* Run along now, boys. The sun's nearly up. Time to get ready. *[To Reporter 1]* Fancy coming along?
Reporter 1	To film?
Odysseus	No, to fight. We need all the help we can get. *[To soldiers]* What do you reckon, boys? Think he'll shape up?
Reporter 1	Er ... much as I'd like to help out ... I really can't get involved ... we have to be impartial.
Odysseus	It's all right. No need to mess your pants. Just another joke. We couldn't use you anyway. *[To soldiers]* Let's go, boys.

*The soldiers exit, **Odysseus** following them. **Reporter 1** calls after him.*

Reporter 1	Lord Odysseus, before you go, would you care to say a few words? Your thoughts on the battle? The war in general?
Odysseus	All right. Why not? *[To audience]* I don't mind admitting I had my doubts about this war in the beginning. It didn't make much sense to me. But I'd pledged my support and went along with it. And in my book, when you commit to something you commit all the way, right to the end. We've been here too long, invested too much. Too many of our men have died. The burning ruins of Troy will be their monument. When that's achieved, then we'll go home.

Odysseus exits.

Reporter 1   The Greek commander Odysseus, there, speaking from the allied camp, as the sun rises on the Trojan plain. Back to the studio.

The television studio.

Phoebe   The sun is rising.

Perses   Preparations are underway.

Phoebe   Soon the battle will begin.

Perses   A battle that may well decide the outcome of this epic war.

Phoebe   A war between the great powers of the west and the east.

Perses   For Achilles, a war for vengeance.

Phoebe   For Hector, a war for the life of Troy.

Perses   Which of these two great powers will prove the victor?

Phoebe   Which of these two great heroes will prevail?

Perses   Stay with *Troy 24* and you'll be the first to find out.

Troy 24 theme tune fades in.

Announcer 1	This is *Troy 24* from Olympian Broadcasting.
Announcer 2	From dusk till dawn, reporting on the action.
Announcer 1	*Troy 24*, all day, every day.
Announcer 2	*Troy 24* – because war never sleeps.

*Music ends. Announcers exit. **Professor Omeros** has entered.*

Phoebe	In a short while we'll be going live to the Trojan plain to bring you coverage of the battle as it happens, as well as comment and analysis here in the studio.
Perses	And to help us with that, we've been joined once again by our expert on the war, Professor Omeros. *[To **Omeros**]* Professor, any pre-battle thoughts?
Phoebe	Achilles or Hector? Which one will it be?
Omeros	Well, it is a close match. Both are the best of their kind – and interestingly, in all the nine years of the war, this is the first time they will have met in combat.
Perses	If they do meet.
Omeros	Oh, I think Achilles will make sure that they do. In fact, I think we shall see some particularly savage fighting today. As far as Achilles is concerned, the gloves are off. After all, with Patroclus dead, and his belief that he will die at Troy, there's nothing for him to lose. And that's why I believe he will win.
Phoebe	Thanks for that insight, Professor. *[To audience]* The day of battle has dawned. But what kind of day is it going to be? Here's Iris with the weather.

Iris enters. A map of the area around Troy appears on the screen.

Iris. How's the weather looking today?

Iris	Around the immediate area of conflict it's looking very good. Even though the sun has only just started to rise, it's already feeling very warm out there on the plain. As you know, it's

quite a sun-trap down there, so we can expect to see some very high temperatures by the middle of the day.

Phoebe	Which is when we can expect the battle to be at its fiercest. Looks like they'll find be finding it pretty uncomfortable.
Iris	I should think so, Phoebe, although there might be a little relief in the form of a westerly breeze blowing in off the Aegean a little later on.
Phoebe	What about further afield?
Iris	Well, that's where we might run into a bit of trouble. A little further to the southeast we have some heavy storm clouds gathering over Mount Ida, and we're already experiencing some electrical storms there. And if that brings heavy rain, it could mean a rise in the level of the two rivers that run down onto the plain, so we might see some flooding there.
Phoebe	But everything's remaining clear over the battlefield itself.
Iris	As far as we can tell, yes. Clear skies and wall-to-wall sunshine. But do keep an eye on those storms. And there's your weather for today.
Phoebe	Thanks, Iris.

Iris exits. The map remains on screen.

Perses	A fine day for a battle, a momentous day for the Greeks and the Trojans. And for one Greek and one Trojan in particular: Achilles and Hector.
Phoebe	Just before we join our outside broadcast teams, we'll take a final look at the characters of these two adversaries. First, Achilles.

*A spotlight comes up on **Achilles**.*

A born warrior. Proud, vain –

Achilles	The name of Achilles will make this war famous.
Phoebe	– vengeful, merciless –

Achilles	Every Trojan is a dead man! Troy is a city of corpses, a city of ghosts.
Phoebe	– independent, outspoken –
Achilles	You're a strutting, swaggering, big-mouthed idiot, Agamemnon.
Phoebe	– unyielding, unbending –
Achilles	When he smells his ships burning, he'll come to me then, on his knees, begging for help. But he won't get it.
Phoebe	– but who carries within him the knowledge of his own tragic fate.
Achilles	I'll never see my home again. My bones will lie here.
Phoebe	And today he fights for one thing, and for one thing only.
Achilles	Vengeance for the death of Patroclus!
Perses	And now, Hector.

A spotlight comes up on Hector.

	Prince of Troy, defender of his people –
Hector	This is our land, where we were born.
Perses	– respected leader –
Hector	We're rooted to it. It makes us strong.
Perses	– diplomat, peacemaker –
Hector	We don't seek war with the Greeks. It's our hope we can find a peaceful solution.
Perses	– feared man of action –
Hector	But if war comes, we're ready for it.
Perses	– a man of feeling –
Hector	I felt sorry for Patroclus. Admired him too.
Perses	– a ruthless warrior –

Hector	He was a Greek, and he had to die.
Perses	– a man who knows what's at stake in the coming struggle –
Hector	We're fighting for something. Our homes, our families, our way of life.
Perses	– and fights with one thought in mind.
Hector	Troy will prevail.
Phoebe	Achilles and Hector.
Perses	Two warriors, two champions –
Phoebe	– soon to be locked in deadly combat.
Perses	And their day has dawned, their time is here.
Hector	Prepare for battle!
Achilles	Hector will die!

*The lights go out on **Achilles** and **Hector**.*

Phoebe	The sun has risen. The troops are in place.
Perses	*Troy 24* will be bringing you live coverage of the battle throughout the day.
Phoebe	We have news teams in both the Greek and the Trojan camps.
Perses	We have cameras stationed at strategic vantage points throughout the field.
Phoebe	As well as our state-of-the-art satellite tactics camera for an overview of the fighting.
Perses	Whatever happens, we'll have it covered and you'll be the first to know.
Phoebe	So without further ado, it's time to go over to our teams in the field.

Reporter 1 enters.

Reporter 1	Hello, Phoebe. I'm here in the Greek camp where Achilles is preparing to –

Lights on the stage suddenly go out. Only the studio remains lit.

Phoebe	Er ... I'm sorry about that ... we seem to have lost contact with the Greek camp. We'll come back to them in a moment. Perses ... ?
Perses	Yes ... so ... we'll go over instead live to the Trojan camp...

*The stage remains in darkness. We hear **Reporter 2** speaking.*

Reporter 2	It is a thrilling sight, the Trojan troops and their many allies –
Perses	[To **Reporter 2**] Hello?
Reporter 2	[Not hearing **Perses**] – assembled here before the great walls of the city –
Perses	We don't seem to have a picture.
Reporter 2	– with Prince Hector at their head, about to advance down the slope to meet the –

Reporter 2 goes silent. Stage remains dark.

Phoebe	Or sound.
Perses	We seem to have lost temporary contact with both our outside broadcast teams ... and ... er ...
Phoebe	We're sure it is only a temporary hitch, so we'll go to a break and be back with live coverage of the battle very soon.

Troy 24 theme tune fades in.

Phoebe	[In a panic] What's going on?
Perses	I don't know.
Phoebe	Somebody must!
Perses	I'll get on to the control room.

Perses speaks on the phone.

Phoebe	[Shouting] Professor! Professor!

Professor Omeros enters.

Omeros	Yes?
Phoebe	Professor, you've got to help us out.
Omeros	In what way?
Phoebe	You can see what's happened. We've lost contact with Outside Broadcasting.
Omeros	I know – but how can I help?
Phoebe	We need to put something on air until we can go over to the battle again.
Omeros	I still don't see –
Phoebe	I thought maybe you could fill in for us.
Omeros	Fill in? With what?
Phoebe	I don't know. You're the expert. Something else on the background: strategy – something like that.
Omeros	I don't know. It's very short notice.
	Perses puts down the phone.
Perses	They think it's the weather.
Phoebe	The weather?
Perses	That electrical storm. The one Iris told us about.
Phoebe	Get her in here.
Perses	What?
Phoebe	I said get her in here. Quick!
Perses	You can't order me about.
Phoebe	Just do it, will you?
Perses	No. Not if you're going to speak to me like that.
Phoebe	Great. We've got a crisis on our hands and you start losing it.
Perses	Losing it? I'm not losing it! I'm not the one giving everybody orders. If anybody's losing it, it's you!

Phoebe	I'm in perfect control!
Perses	You sound like it.
Phoebe	Look, I'm just asking –
Perses	You didn't ask!
Phoebe	You want me to ask? All right, I'll ask. Perses, will you please find Iris and bring her here?
Perses	What for? She can't do anything about it!
Phoebe	She might be able tell us how long it's going to last!
Perses	Yes. I see. Right. Okay. As you asked.

Perses exits. **Phoebe** *turns to* **Professor Omeros**.

Well, Professor? What have you got?

Omeros	Nothing.
Phoebe	What?
Omeros	I don't have anything prepared. I wasn't expecting this.
Phoebe	None of us were expecting it. But we have to deal with it.
Omeros	I don't see why I should be the one –
Phoebe	For God's sake, not you as well! Is it only me who realizes how serious this situation is?
Omeros	Shouting at everyone isn't going to make it less serious.
Phoebe	But it might get something done!
Omeros	Not from me, it won't. I'm sorry, I can't help.

Professor Omeros turns to exit.

Phoebe	Yes, you can, and you will! It's what you're paid for, Professor. You get a pretty good fee, if I'm not mistaken. So if you want to keep getting it, think of something! And fast!

Perses enters with Iris.

Perses	Here she is.

Phoebe	Iris. This storm –
Iris	I said to keep an eye on it. It seems to be interfering with your communications.
Phoebe	I know that. How long is it going to last?
Iris	Who can say?
Phoebe	*You* can. You do the weather forecast!
Iris	Things like electrical storms are difficult to predict with accuracy.
Phoebe	Try.
Iris	I can't.
Phoebe	A rough guess.
Iris	It could go on all day.
Phoebe	*[Sarcastic]* Thanks. That was really useful.
Iris	I'm sorry. I don't make the weather, you know.
Phoebe	No. You don't make a very good job of presenting it, either.
Iris	There's no need to speak to me like that!
Perses	Don't worry, you're not the only one.
Omeros	You should have heard how she spoke to me.
Phoebe	Are you ready, Professor? We're on air in a couple of minutes.
Omeros	Er . . . yes . . . I do have something. I'll need to use the map *[To Iris]* – if you don't mind.
Phoebe	Of course she doesn't mind. Hasn't got much use for it herself.
Iris	*[Upset]* Really! I – it just isn't – oh!
	Iris exits. **Professor Omeros** *makes his way centre stage.*
Perses	What's going on?
Phoebe	Omeros is filling in for us till we get contact again.

Perses	What's he doing?
Phoebe	Don't know. Don't care. As long as there's something on screen. Nobody ever listens to what he says, anyway.
Perses	I do.
Phoebe	You would. All set, Professor?
Omeros	I suppose so.
Phoebe	Try and be a bit more enthusiastic.
Perses	Here we go.
Phoebe	Right.

Troy 24 music.

Phoebe	*[To audience]* Welcome back. Now, I'm afraid that because we're still experiencing technical problems, we can't take you yet to our live coverage of the battle. But while we're waiting for that, here's some analysis from Professor Omeros.
Omeros	Thank you. As we're all aware, today's battle is crucial. But what makes it so crucial? What exactly is at stake? If we look at Troy's geographical position here on the map, we'll begin to get an idea –

Perses interrupts Professor Omeros.

Perses	I'm sorry, but we're going to have to stop you there, Professor.
Omeros	What?
Perses	We've just heard that we've managed to re-establish contact with our news teams on the battlefield.
Omeros	But –
Phoebe	Sorry, Professor. We'll hear from you later.
Omeros	That's what you think!

Professor Omeros storms off.

Perses	Due to the electrical storm the signal's still a bit patchy, and you may experience some interference.
Phoebe	But without further ado, let's go straight over to our live coverage of the battle.

Blackout.

● ●

SCENE 20

*The battle. A series of short, fragmentary scenes of the battle follow. Each scene is illuminated briefly before the stage goes dark again. Lights go up on **Hector**, **Aeneas**, **Sarpedon**, **Euphemus** and **Acamas** grouped together.*

Hector	Aeneas, Euphemus, take charge of the left flank. Glaucus, Acamas, take the right.
Aeneas	And you?
Hector	I'll wait here. Let him come to me.
Euphemus	While we move down and round.
Acamas	Close the circle behind him.
Sarpedon	Trap him inside.
Aeneas	And you finish him off.
Hector	That's the plan. If it works. Ready? Let's go!

*Blackout. Lights up on **Reporter 1**. On the screen we can see the shadow of **Achilles**.*

Reporter 1	Directly ahead I can see Achilles in his chariot at the head of his troops. One arm is raised, gripping his spear. The bright sunlight flashes from his armour, giving him an almost godlike appearance. The horses stamp and snort, impatient to be off. And now Achilles gives a great cry, and plunges forward into the battle. And with a roar of voices and a clash of weapons, the Greek army races after him, as the whole plain thunders with horses and men.

*Blackout. Lights up on **Reporter 2**.*

Reporter 2	As you can hear, the battle's underway, though from where I'm standing I can't see a great deal of it. I can just make out the Trojan right flank moving onto –
	Thersites runs on, interrupting him.
Thersites	Here, come with me.
Reporter 2	What?
Thersites	Come with me, I said.
Reporter 2	I'm in the middle of a broadcast.
Thersites	I can get you a better view of the battle.
Reporter 2	Can you?
Thersites	I know just the place. Right in the thick of it. But safe.
Reporter 2	Who are you?
Thersites	What do I look like?
Reporter 2	A Greek soldier. Aren't you supposed to be fighting?
Thersites	Fighting's for mugs. Do you want a better view?
Reporter 2	Yes.
Thersites	Come on, then.
Reporter 2	Right.
Thersites	It'll cost you, mind.
Reporter 2	How much?
Thersites	We'll discuss that on the way. It'll be worth it. You'll get some great shots. Probably get an award, as well. Is it a deal?
Reporter 2	It's a deal. *[To audience]* I'll be back in a few –
Thersites	No time for that. You'll miss the action. Come on!
	Thersites drags Reporter 2 off stage. Blackout. Lights up on Achilles and a Trojan soldier. The soldier is kneeling before Achilles, begging for mercy.

Trojan	Spare me!
Achilles	Why should I?
Trojan	My father's rich. Take me prisoner and he'll pay a ransom for me.
Achilles	How much?
Trojan	Whatever you ask.
Achilles	Enough to bring back the dead?
Trojan	No.
Achilles	Then he can keep it.
Trojan	Please – I'm my mother's only son!
Achilles	So am I. And we'll both die here at Troy.

Achilles raises his sword to strike. Blackout. Lights up on Reporter 1 who is in mid broadcast.

Reporter 1 . . . soldiers in panic trying to cross the river which is already swollen with corpses, its waters red with the blood of the slain. And Achilles wades among them, striking to right and left, killing all he finds, and their bodies join the others in the river, piling higher and higher against the current.

69

*Lights up on **Euphemus** and **Acamas**.*

Euphemus	Our flank's broken.
Acamas	Ours too.
Euphemus	Hector's still holding.
Acamas	Where's Aeneas?
Euphemus	The last I saw, trying to cut his way through to Achilles.
Acamas	Glaucus is dead. Ajax killed him.

*Ajax and **Diomedes** enter from other side of stage.*

Ajax	And now he'll kill you.
Diomedes	And I will take the other.
Ajax	Don't think of running.
Diomedes	There's nowhere to run to.
Ajax	Stand and fight.
Diomedes	And die like men.

*The four prepare to fight. Blackout. Lights up on **Hector**. **Aeneas** enters.*

Aeneas	We'll have to pull back.
Hector	No.
Aeneas	There's nothing else we can do.
Hector	We can stand our ground.
Aeneas	And fight alone? The men are falling back already.
Hector	Let them. I won't fall back.
Aeneas	We've lost this battle but we can still win the war.
Hector	The war's dragged on too long.
Aeneas	Without you Troy falls.

Hector	Without Achilles the Greeks are lost. Him or me. Let it be settled today.
Aeneas	Hector –
Hector	Rally our troops, cousin. Lead them back to the city. I know they're safe in your hands. Go now, before he comes.
Aeneas	I'll see you back there.
Hector	Or some other place.

*Aeneas exits. **Hector** turns to face the audience. Lights up on **Reporter 2**.*

Reporter 2	All around me the Trojans are fleeing –

*A **Trojan soldier** runs on.*

Trojan 1	Get out of here!

*The **soldier** runs off.*

Reporter 2	– making their way back to the city –

*A second **Trojan soldier** runs on.*

Trojan 2	The Greeks are coming!

*The **soldier** runs off.*

Reporter 2	– and I can now see the Greek army in pursuit, coming up the hill towards the citadel.

*A third **Trojan soldier** runs on.*

Trojan 3	They're killing anything that moves!
Reporter 2	I'm a reporter –
Trojan 3	Anything that isn't Greek!

***Trojan 3** makes to run off but is prevented by the entrance of two Greek soldiers.*

Greek 1	And you're not.

Greek 2	So you're dead.
	*They kill the **Trojan soldier**.*
Reporter 2	Did you get that? A Trojan cut down, right in front of us. And this kind of thing is happening everywhere I look, as the Greeks swarm over the hill –
	*The soldiers turn their attention to **Reporter 2**.*
	– showing no mercy, giving no quarter –
Greek 1	No quarter. Right.
Reporter 2	*[To the soldiers]* I'm a reporter.
Greek 2	No mercy. Spot on.
Reporter 2	For *Troy 24* – war correspondent.
Greek 1	So you're not Greek.
Greek 2	*[Indicating the dead Trojan]* And you heard what he said.
Reporter 2	I have immunity –
Greek 1	Not from us you don't.
Greek 2	See what your viewers think of this.
Greek 1	You'll probably get an award.
Greek 2	Posthumous.
	*They close in on **Reporter 2** and raise their swords to kill him. He cries out. Blackout.*

● ●

SCENE 21

The television studio.

Perses	*[To audience, hesitating]* That was live coverage from today's battle . . . which we seem to have lost again . . . due to technical difficulties . . .
Phoebe	But we hope to be returning there shortly . . . after this break.

Music: Troy 24 theme tune.

*[To **Perses**]* Damn! We've lost it again! I'll see what's going on.

Phoebe *picks up the phone.*

Perses	Did you see what happened?
Phoebe	*[Talking on the phone]* What's going on?
Perses	Did you see what they did?
Phoebe	... I thought you'd got it back.
Perses	They killed him. In front of our eyes.
Phoebe	... Yes, I know that.
Perses	On camera.
Phoebe	... Well, how long?
Perses	As if they didn't care who saw.
Phoebe	... Okay. Let me know as soon as you have.
Perses	As if they wanted it to be seen.
Phoebe	... He's what?
Perses	Like it was – some kind of warning.
Phoebe	... Down here? Great!
Perses	A warning to us.
Phoebe	... Thanks for letting me know. *[Putting down the phone]* Guess who's on his way down? The Boss. He's here, and he's coming down to the studio.
Perses	Don't you care?
Phoebe	Of course I care! He's not going to be very happy about all this, is he?
Perses	I mean, what they did! The last thing we saw. You did see it, didn't you? You saw what they did?

Phoebe	Yes. I saw. But –
Perses	We ought to do something about it.
Phoebe	Do what? It's war.
Perses	I know. But they're not supposed to do things like that.
Phoebe	Looks like somebody forgot to tell them.
Perses	You don't care, do you?
Phoebe	I care. But right now I have a job to do. And so do you. And the Boss is coming down –
Perses	Yes, I heard you say.
Phoebe	Look. I know how you feel. It was a terrible thing. Really . . . unfortunate.
Perses	Unfortunate!

The Boss enters.

The Boss	It was more than unfortunate. It was downright negligent. As well as stupid. He got in too close, took a risk, and it didn't pay off. We did get some good footage, though.
Phoebe	Boss! This is a pleasant surprise.
The Boss	No it's not. They probably told you upstairs I was coming down. And it's not going to be pleasant, either.
Perses	They killed him!
The Boss	Yes. And his sacrifice will be acknowledged. We'll give him an award, our highest honour. Posthumous. And his wife – was he married?
Phoebe	I don't know.
The Boss	If he was married his wife will get a good pension. We look after our staff and their families here at Olympian Broadcasting. And we expect one hundred per cent dedication in return.
Phoebe	That's what you get from us.

The Boss	Is it? I'm not so sure about that at the moment.
Phoebe	We're doing our best, sir, but it's the weather. It's pretty bad. *[To Perses]* Isn't it?
Perses	It's very bad. An electrical storm.
The Boss	I know it's an electrical storm. But what are you doing about it?
Phoebe	There's not much we can do about the weather, sir.
The Boss	You can do something about what happens in here! And what *is* happening? Nothing! What do you have lined up for after the break? Eh?
Phoebe	We were just putting our minds to that.
The Boss	This channel built its reputation on the war. It has a commitment to cover the war, 24 hours a day, seven days a week! To bring it live into viewers' homes. It's what they pay their subscriptions for. And those subscriptions pay your salaries. Very good salaries too. If we don't deliver, they turn off, cancel their subscriptions. The channel loses viewing figures, I lose my reputation, and you lose your jobs!
Perses	We could always bring Omeros back on.
The Boss	And send everybody to sleep?
Phoebe	*[Jokingly]* Or pray . . .
The Boss	Maybe you better had! You'd better come up with something! Achilles is about to kill Hector. It's the highlight of the week! The month! Maybe the whole campaign. And we could miss it!
Perses	He might not.
The Boss	What?
Perses	Kill him. Achilles might not kill Hector.
The Boss	Of course he will. He has to. Everyone expects it. He's crazy, I know, probably psychotic. But he's a crowd-puller. And he's Greek, on the winning side.

Perses	We don't know who's going to win.
The Boss	Yes, we do. It's all being decided today. Hector will die, and Troy will fall. Not straight away of course. Achilles has to go first. Even things out again, build up the tension. Say about a year. But at last, the Greeks finally break in, burn the city, pull it down to the ground. Imagine the viewing figures for that! They'll go through the roof! And then a final shot. An empty shoreline, waves washing over the sand. In the distance, on the hill, smoke rising from the ruins of the once proud city. And here, right in front of us, in close-up, lying on the beach, a single upturned helmet. All that remains. Fade to black out.
Phoebe	I can see it!
The Boss	So can I.
Phoebe	And it's all over.
The Boss	The viewers think it's all over, but it's not. The Greeks have to get home. That won't be as easy as they think. Storms! Shipwrecks! Adventures in foreign lands. Rebellion at home! We'll follow it all! Satellite cameras, teams in every ship, you in the studio. We can keep it going for years!
Phoebe	It's brilliant!
The Boss	I know.
Phoebe	You ought to get a knighthood for this, sir.
The Boss	I intend to.
	The phone rings.
	[To Phoebe] The phone.
Phoebe	What? Oh –
	Phoebe quickly picks up the phone.
The Boss	You'd better hope it's good news.

Perses	*[To **The Boss**]* You're speaking as if you know what's going happen. As if it's all been arranged, sir.
The Boss	It is, more less. It took a lot of preparation, groundwork, planning. That's what this business is all about. It's not enough to report the news. You have to make it.
Phoebe	We're back in contact. We can go live again.
The Boss	Looks like the praying worked. I'll leave you to it, then. You're doing a good job. A great job. Well done. Keep it up.
	***The Boss** exits.*
Perses	Did you hear all that?
Phoebe	Hear what?
Perses	What the boss was saying.
Phoebe	No. I was on the phone.
Perses	He said –
Phoebe	We're back on – now!
	[To audience] Welcome back. We're pleased to tell you that we can now bring you more live coverage of the battle, which appears to be approaching its climax.
Perses	So, over now live to Troy.

• •

SCENE 22

*Lights up on **Hector** as we last saw him, standing facing the audience. **Achilles** enters.*

Achilles	Hector. Turn and fight.
	***Hector** turns to face **Achilles**.*
Hector	I'm ready.
Achilles	To die?
Hector	That's the risk we both take.

Achilles	The fate of all men.
Hector	Especially our kind.
Achilles	But we're different, you and I.
Hector	How?
Achilles	I hate. You don't. That's why today you'll die.
Hector	If not now, later.
Achilles	Not later. Now. *[Taking up a fighting stance]* Let's fight.
Hector	And may the best man win.
Achilles	Oh, the best man will.

*They prepare to fight. Suddenly, we hear **Patroclus's** voice, spoken off stage.*

Patroclus	Fate's coming for you. You won't live long. I see death on your back.

Hector falters, looks around.

Hector	What?

*Four Greek soldiers enter and surround **Hector**.*

This is no fair fight.

Achilles	Who said I was fair? I don't want to be fair. I want you to die.
Hector	So that's the way it is.
Achilles	Yes.
Hector	Achilles, promise me this. When you've killed me, give my body back to Troy. Let my parents bury it with full rites and honours.
Achilles	I'll make you this promise. When you're dead I'll tie your body to my chariot. I'll drag it around the city for all to see. Then I'll leave it in the dust to rot, and the dogs will drink your blood and eat your bones.

*He nods to the soldiers. They close in around **Hector**, strike him, and he falls.*

I'll finish him off.

*The soldiers part. **Achilles** approaches.*

Goodbye, Hector.

*He kills **Hector**.*

He's dead. Now let Troy weep. Let Troy howl. Troy will burn, and Troy will die. Nothing will remain but ghosts and old stones. And still it won't be over.

*Lights fade slowly until only **Achilles** is visible, alone onstage.*

SCENE 23

The television studio.

Perses   That was murder.

Phoebe   That was war. They're the same thing.

Perses   It was a trick. That thing with Patroclus's voice. It was a recording.

Phoebe	What are you talking about?
Perses	He fixed it!
Phoebe	Who did?
Perses	The Boss. He fixed the whole thing. Hector's death, the whole war. It's what he was saying: it's not enough to report the news, you have to make it.
Phoebe	He's right.
Perses	I'm not sure I want to be part of this anymore.
Phoebe	What?

Perses stands up.

Perses	This job. It's not worth it.
Phoebe	You're just going to walk out? Leave me to it?
Perses	You'll manage.
Phoebe	It won't change anything you know. If you go. They'll just find somebody else. The war will still be there. We're back on air in a minute. If you are leaving you'd better go now. Or stay. It's up to you. We're on now.

*Music. **Perses** glumly sits back down.*

[To audience] A dramatic end there to a dramatic day. Hector, prince and champion of Troy, is dead. Now it seems only a matter of time before the city falls, and the Greeks are victorious. Perses.

*She looks across at **Perses**.*

Perses	*[Pause, then wearily]* So it would appear, Phoebe. But as we all know from past experience, there's nothing about this war that can be taken for granted. If Troy is doomed to fall, how long will it take for that to come about?
Phoebe	Will Troy perhaps find a new champion?
Perses	Is Achilles himself doomed, as he appears to believe?

Phoebe	And can anyone really predict with certainty what the outcome will be?
Perses	Whatever happens, *Troy 24* will be here to bring you the action as it happens.
	Announcers enter.
Announcer 1	The news and the views.
Announcer 2	The comments and analysis.
Announcer 1	*Troy 24* – the action station.
Announcer 2	*Troy 24* – bringing the war home to you.
Phoebe	Don't go away.
Perses	We'll be back after the break.
	Lights fade on studio. **Achilles** *is left alone in spotlight.*
Achilles	And still it won't be over.
	Blackout.

THE END

Activities

Year 7

KEY STAGE 3 FRAMEWORK OBJECTIVES	RELEVANT ACTIVITIES CHAPTER(S)
Reading	
1 Locate information	Who's who?; 'Two warriors, two champions'; Researching and retelling classic tales
2 Extract information	Time line of events; 'Two warriors, two champions'; Researching and retelling classic tales
4 Note-making	Who's who?; Time line of events; 'Two warriors, two champions'; Researching and retelling classic tales
7 Identify main ideas	Time line of events
8 Infer and deduce	'Two warriors, two champions'; *The Iliad*: an epic poem
12 Character, setting and mood	*The Iliad*: an epic poem
18 Response to a play	'Two warriors, two champions'; *The Iliad*: an epic poem
19 Poetic form	*The Iliad*: an epic poem
20 Literary heritage	*The Iliad*: an epic poem
Speaking and Listening	
1 Clarify through talk	Who's who?; Time line of events; 'Two warriors, two champions'; OBC (Olympian Broadcasting Company); Making or reporting news?
5 Put a point of view	Making or reporting news?
6 Recall main points	Making or reporting news?
7 Pertinent questions	Making or reporting news?
8 Presentational techniques	OBC (Olympian Broadcasting Company)
10 Report main points	OBC (Olympian Broadcasting Company)
11 Range of roles	OBC (Olympian Broadcasting Company); Making or reporting news?
12 Exploratory talk	'Two warriors, two champions'; Making or reporting news?
13 Collaboration	Time line of events; 'Two warriors, two champions'; OBC (Olympian Broadcasting Company); Making or reporting news?
14 Modify views	Time line of events; 'Two warriors, two champions'; OBC (Olympian Broadcasting Company); Making or reporting news?
15 Explore in role	'Two warriors, two champions'; OBC (Olympian Broadcasting Company); *The Iliad*: an epic poem
16 Collaborate on scripts	'Two warriors, two champions'; OBC (Olympian Broadcasting Company)
17 Extend spoken repertoire	OBC (Olympian Broadcasting Company)
18 Exploratory drama	*The Iliad*: an epic poem
19 Evaluate presentations	'Two warriors, two champions'; OBC (Olympian Broadcasting Company); Making or reporting news?

Writing

1	Drafting process	Researching and retelling classic tales
2	Planning formats	Researching and retelling classic tales
5	Story structure	Time line of events; Researching and retelling classic tales
6	Characterization	Time line of events; Researching and retelling classic tales
7	Narrative devices	Time line of events
8	Visual and sound effects	Researching and retelling classic tales
9	Link writing and reading	Researching and retelling classic tales

Word Level

15	Dictionary and thesaurus	*The Iliad*: an epic poem
21	Subject vocabulary	*The Iliad*: an epic poem
22	Words in different languages	*The Iliad*: an epic poem

TROY 24 ACTIVITIES

Year 8

KEY STAGE 3 FRAMEWORK OBJECTIVES	RELEVANT ACTIVITIES CHAPTER(S)
Reading	
2 Independent research	Researching and retelling classic tales
3 Notemaking formats	Who's who?; Time line of events; Researching and retelling classic tales
5 Trace developments	Time line of events
4 Versatile reading	'Two warriors, two champions'
5 Trace developments	'Two warriors, two champions'
6 Bias and objectivity	'Two warriors, two champions'
8 Transposition	*The Iliad*: an epic poem
10 Development of key ideas	Time line of events
11 Compare treatments of the same theme	*The Iliad*: an epic poem
14 Literary conventions	*The Iliad*: an epic poem
15 Historical context	*The Iliad*: an epic poem
16 Cultural context	*The Iliad*: an epic poem
Speaking and Listening	
1 Evaluate own speaking	Making or reporting news?
3 Formal presentation	Making or reporting news?
4 Commentary	OBC (Olympian Broadcasting Company)
5 Questions to clarify	Who's who?; OBC (Olympian Broadcasting Company); Making or reporting news?
2 Develop recount	'Two warriors, two champions'
3 Formal presentation	'Two warriors, two champions'
5 Questions to clarify or refine	'Two warriors, two champions'
7 Listen for a specific purpose	'Two warriors, two champions'; Making or reporting news?
8 Hidden messages	'Two warriors, two champions'
9 Evaluate own contributions	Making or reporting news?
10 Hypothesis and speculation	OBC (Olympian Broadcasting Company)
11 Building on others	'Two warriors, two champions'; OBC (Olympian Broadcasting Company); Making or reporting news?
12 Varied roles in discussion	OBC (Olympian Broadcasting Company); Making or reporting news?
14 Dramatic techniques	'Two warriors, two champions'; *The Iliad*: an epic poem
15 Work in role	'Two warriors, two champions'; OBC (Olympian Broadcasting Company)
16 Collaborative presentation	'Two warriors, two champions'; OBC (Olympian Broadcasting Company); *The Iliad*: an epic poem

Writing

1	Effective planning	Researching and retelling classic tales
2	Anticipate reader reaction	Researching and retelling classic tales
6	Figurative language	Researching and retelling classic tales
7	Establish the tone	Time line of events
8	Experiment with conventions	Researching and retelling classic tales
9	Rework in different forms	Researching and retelling classic tales
10	Hypothesis and speculation	Time line of events
11	Building on others	Time line of events

Word Level

6c	Dictionaries	*The Iliad*: and epic poem
6f	Word formation	*The Iliad*: and epic poem

Who's who?

· ·

There are many characters in this play. The Greeks and Trojans are all characters described in the ancient epic poem, *The Iliad,* written by Homer. The reporters and presenters of the news channel are all new characters. The playwright has added them to tell the story in a more modern way.

Copy and complete the two grids on pages 88 and 89, to help you understand who is who among the Greeks and Trojans.

- Write in note form, using key words and phrases, rather than full sentences.
- Try to explain the characters in your own words first. Add a little bit about their personality and what they actually do in the play.
- Flick through the play to find details about your characters.
- Use the character list on pages 8 and 9 to check your information.

Greek characters	Who they are
Menelaus	
Agamemnon	
Achilles	
Patroclus	
Odysseus	

Trojan characters	Who they are
Hector	
Aeneas	
Helen	
Paris	
Priam	

THE GUESSING GAME

When you have completed your grids, share them with a partner. You might want to add information to your grid if your partner has noted something that you haven't.

Then, play the guessing game:

1 One person (silently) chooses to be a character, either a Trojan or Greek.
2 The other person has to ask questions to try to find out which character it is.
3 The first person can only answer 'yes' or 'no'.
4 – The second person asks questions such as:
   – Are you Greek?
   – Do you die in this play?
   – Do you fight in this play?
   – Are you a king?
5 Make a note of how many questions are asked before the person guesses the correct character.
6 Swap over, so each person takes a turn choosing a character and asking questions. Do this as many times as you like, giving each person the same number of turns.
7 The winner is the person who guesses the correct character with the least number of questions.

Time line of events

• •

Some writers tell their story as a sequence of events, starting with what happened at the beginning, then explaining what happened next, and finishing with what happened in the end. Other writers prefer to start their stories in the middle, often at a dramatic point, and then explain what happened before and after.

In this play, the playwright starts the story not at the beginning, but near the end. He has chosen a dramatic, action-packed scene to grab the reader's attention. Scene 1 is the fight between Hector and Patroclus. The reader is immediately 'hooked' by the violent drama and high emotion. Our curiosity is aroused and there are lots of questions that we want answers to. For example:

● Why is one soldier disguised as another?
● Why are these two men fighting?
● What does the reporter mean when he says 'all will be decided by single combat between these two champions'?
● Is Patroclus actually killed?

To answer these questions, the reader must read on. It is only as the play unfolds that we learn what happened before and then what happens next.

Here are some of the events in the play. We learn about them at different points in the play, but not always in the order in which they happen.

● With a partner, put the events in sequence on the time line. The first event should be at the top and the last event at the bottom.
● Choose two more events in the play that could be added to the time line.
● You might find it helpful to copy and cut out the events and move them around the time line, until you are sure about the sequence.

Time line

↓

Achilles kills Hector

Helen and Paris confess their love for each other

Helen is interviewed, after nine years in Troy

Paris and Agamemnon declare war.

Patroclus's body is taken to Achilles

Chryseis is captured and plague hits the Greek army

Hector kills Patroclus

Achilles argues with Agamemnon

↓

A GRIPPING OPENING

Think up your own story opening, which would grip a reader with its drama and tension. Remember, this sort of opening is effective if:

● the characters show a high level of emotion
● there is physical action
● questions spring into the reader's mind, so they want to read on.

Here are a couple of examples:

She hurled the chains at me, eyes flashing, screaming in a shrill, furious voice, 'Tell me, or you will die!'

I had no choice, whatever they said. It was now or never. As I raised my fists the chanting grew louder...

'Two warriors, two champions'

Hector and Achilles are champion warriors. In their final fight, they represent their two different armies. Both are determined to win, but are also prepared to die.

Choose either Hector or Achilles and prepare to give a press conference, in role. The role of the warriors can be played by girls and boys. Think carefully about your chosen character. Refer to the play to answer these questions:

- How does he treat his soldiers?
- Does he inspire loyalty and friendship?
- Is he thoughtful or quick to anger?
- What does he think of himself?
- What makes him want to fight? (Look at pages 53 to 54 for Hector and page 44 for Achilles.)

With a partner, think about how your character might walk, sit and stand. What sort of expressions might be in his face? What gestures might he use? What sort of voice might he have? With a partner, practise how you might convey your character through your physical presence, as well as through what you say.

THE PRESS CONFERENCE

Imagine it is just before the final fight. Hector and Achilles have both agreed to give a short press conference (separately). Arrange the group or class as if at a press conference.

1   The warrior will walk into the room, accompanied by an aid* and sit down at the front of the class, facing the reporters.

* The aid could be the partner who advised on the presentation of the character. As the aid, he or she can give quiet prompts to the warrior during the interview.

2   The warrior will stand up and give a short statement about what is about to happen and why they have agreed to fight.

3   Reporters will raise their hands if they have a question, and the warrior will choose to answer four questions. Then the warrior will leave the 'stage'.

4   The reporters (the rest of the group or class) then talk about the role play, highlighting two good aspects of the role, and another aspect that could be improved.

5   The student who acted as warrior says one thing that they felt they did well to convey the character, and one thing that they could improve.

OBC (Olympian Broadcasting Company)

The playwright uses the OBC to give a modern slant to the telling of this ancient tale about the Trojan War. There are many advantages of using this technique:

- The news is constantly updated, so we can follow the events as they happen.
- Presenters link together all the bits of information.
- Reporters at the scene of the action give their immediate impressions.
- Key people can be interviewed.
- Experts give detailed information and background to events.
- The news is broken up into chunks, interspersed with weather reports and commercial breaks.

THE TROJAN HORSE ON *TROY 24*

Plan and act out your own OBC broadcast. Focus on another episode in the Trojan War – the Trojan Horse, which is mentioned in several other ancient epic stories.

The main points of the story are:

1 It's near the end of the war. The Greek warrior Odysseus orders a huge wooden horse to be built. It is hollow, so soldiers can hide in it.
2 When the horse is built, Odysseus and his soldiers get inside. The rest of the Greek army pretend to sail away from Troy, although they really just hide nearby.
3 One Greek, Sinon, stays with the horse. When the Trojans come to admire the great horse, he pretends to be angry that the Greeks have deserted him.
4 The Trojans think that they have won the war and the horse has been left as a gift. Sinon encourages them to take it into their city.

95

5   That night, the Trojans feast and drink to celebrate what they think is their victory. But in the middle of the night, when everyone is asleep, Sinon opens the horse and lets out the Greek soliders. They open the city gates to the rest of the Greek army, who storm the city, killing the Trojan men, and taking the women and children as slaves.

6   Troy is defeated, and this marks the end of the ten-year Trojan War.

Cast list

Plan how your group will cover this story (as part of a *Troy 24* broadcast). Choose one person in your group to make notes for the cast list and another to make notes for the coverage of the event. Appoint a chairperson, who should ensure that everyone has a chance to put forward his or her ideas and suggestions.

If the group cannot agree on something, the chairperson organizes a vote on the issue.

First, you will need to decide on your cast list. This might include:

- Two presenters: Phoebe and Perses
- Professor Omeros
- Reporter 1 (reporting from the Greek camp)
- Reporter 2 (reporting from inside Troy)
- Two station announcers (see page 19)
- Odysseus
- Sinon
- Priam (King of Troy)
- Greek soldiers
- Trojan citizens, men, women and children.

Next, you need to plan the coverage of the event. You might include:

- Speculation about what the Greeks are building
- Discussion about why the Greeks appear to be leaving

- Reports on the appearance of the horse and how the Trojans react to it
- Secret footage from inside the Trojan Horse
- Reports on the Trojan celebrations
- An interview with Odysseus after the event.

Once parts and coverage have been agreed, split into smaller groups to rehearse individual reports and interviews.

You may wish to script what you are going to say, in which case make sure everyone has a copy of the final script. Or you may wish to improvise, developing ideas as you go along.

Present your broadcast to other students. Afterwards, ask them to comment on what they think were the good things about your broadcast and what you could improve on.

Making or reporting news?

The owner of *Troy 24* says 'It's not enough to report the news. You have to make it.' Do you agree with this view? Hold a class debate, using evidence from the text to support your views.

First, look closely at three extracts of the play which show that the Boss is manipulating the news, i.e. paying someone (Thersites) to make things happen which are used to make exciting TV footage.

a) In Scene 12, Thersites tells Phoebe and Persus that he was paid to make the secret film of Achilles and Patroclus. He explains that he got the camera from a cameraman who was 'accidentally' killed on the battlefield.

b) In Scene 20, Thersites takes a reporter into the battlefield, promising him protection, but a great view. It turns out that the reporter is left to be killed by the advancing Greek soldiers, all of which is recorded on film.

c) In Scene 21, the Boss shrugs off the reporter's death, and says 'We did get some good footage.' He also says 'That's what this business is all about.' He is far more concerned about the media coverage of the war, than any human suffering.

Then follow the steps below to hold a debate.

Step 1
Split into two groups: those who agree with the Boss's view and those that disagree.

Step 2
Appoint an impartial chairperson, who will have authority to say who can speak when.

Step 3
Each group should appoint a spokesperson to represent their views.

Step 4

Each group should discuss their viewpoint and draw up a list of arguments to support it.* They should also try to anticipate what their opponents might say, and think of counter-arguments.

Step 5

Each speaker presents his or her viewpoint. Some notes made during Step 4 may be useful to have.

Step 6

The chairperson 'opens the floor' to other viewpoints – letting everyone have their say.

Step 7

A vote is taken. The side with most votes wins.

After the debate, think about how you contributed to both the group discussion and the debate itself. Make a note of what you think you did well and what you could improve upon next time.

* Below are some areas to explore when drawing up arguments in Step 4.

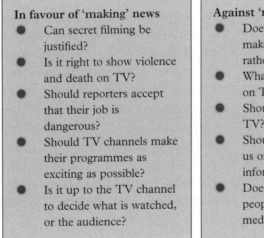

In favour of 'making' news	Against 'making' news
● Can secret filming be justified?	● Does 'exciting' reporting make things seem fictional rather than real?
● Is it right to show violence and death on TV?	● What effect does violence on TV have on viewers?
● Should reporters accept that their job is dangerous?	● Should death be shown on TV?
● Should TV channels make their programmes as exciting as possible?	● Should the news entertain us or just give information?
● Is it up to the TV channel to decide what is watched, or the audience?	● Does secret filming make people distrust the media?

The Iliad: an epic poem

The Iliad (on which Troy 24 is based) is an epic poem.

● What do you think the word 'epic' means? Share your thoughts with a partner and jot down some ideas.
● Use a dictionary to check the meaning of 'epic'.

The word 'epic' comes from the Greek word *epos*, meaning 'song'. In ancient times, epic poems would have been sung to an audience.

Here is an extract from The Iliad. It has been translated from Greek into English. It describes the final fight between Hector and Achilles.

> Now in his heart
> the Trojan [1] realized the truth and said:
> 'This is the end. The gods are calling deathward...
> the appointed time is upon me. Still, I would not
> die without delivering a stroke,
> or die ingloriously, but in some action
> memorable to men in days to come.'
>   With this he drew the whetted[2] blade that hung
> upon his left flank, ponderous and long,
> collecting all his might the way an eagle
> narrows himself to dive through shady cloud
> and strike a lamb or cowering hare: so Hector
> lanced ahead and swung his whetted blade.
> Achilles with wild fury in his heart
> pulled in upon his chest his beautiful shield –
> his helmet with four burnished[3] metal ridges
> nodding above it, and the golden crest

1 Hector
2 sharpened
3 polished

Hephaestus[4] locked there tossing in the wind.
Conspicuous as the evening star that comes,
amid the first in heaven, at fall of night,
and stands most lovely in the west, so shone
in sunlight the fine-pointed spear
Achilles poised in his right hand, with deadly
aim at Hector, at the skin where most
it lay exposed. But nearly all was covered
by the bronze gear he took from slain Patroclus,
Showing only, where his collar-bones
divided neck and shoulders, the bare throat
where the destruction of a life is quickest.
Here, then, as the Trojan charged, Achilles
drove his point straight through the tender neck. . .

From Homer's *The Iliad*, translated by Robert Fitzgerald,
Oxford World's Classics

- Hector realizes that he is going to die. Look carefully at what he says. What does he hope for after his death?
- What image describes Hector before he attacks? Why is it appropriate?
- What is Achilles's spear compared to? What image is created in the reader's mind?
- How does Hector's death differ in *Troy 24*? Why do you think the playwright changed it slightly?

● ●

FREEZE FRAMES

Create two freeze frames. Each shows a moment, frozen in time, of the final fight:

1   The first freeze frame should show the final moments between Achilles and Hector in *The Iliad*. Two people take the role of the warriors. Each should be poised for attack, using the descriptions in the epic poem.

4 the god who made Achilles's helmet

2   The second freeze frame should show the final moments between Achilles, four Greek soldiers and Hector in *Troy 24* (see Scene 22). Six students take these roles. Select the moment you want to 'freeze' carefully.

When both freeze frames have been set up, other students should take turns to tap one of the actors on the shoulder. That actor has to describe, briefly, what he or she is doing and what he or she is feeling.

Researching and retelling classic tales

Stories have been told for thousands of years. Some are so popular that they have been passed from generation to generation, finding a new audience every time they are told.

Early stories were told verbally. Many would be sung or chanted, to help the storytellers remember the words. Others would be told as a narrative, and often the details would be changed slightly by different storytellers.

As more people learned to read and write, the stories were written down. This helped to keep some details fixed, but it did not stop writers re-telling the stories in different ways. Writers tell stories for different audiences, for example, for children, teenagers or adults. Nowadays, stories can be written for radio, television or films. They can be in the form of poems, plays or novels.

Choose an ancient, classic tale and retell it in a different form, for an audience of your choice.

RESEARCH

Do some research to find out about an ancient classic tale. You might choose one of the following:

- Helen of Troy and Paris
- Icarus, who tried to fly
- Perseus and Medusa
- Theseus and the Minotaur

Use a variety of resources for your research, including the Internet and books. You might also like to find some pictures, to help you write descriptions of characters or places.

Make notes to record what you find. Use spider diagrams,

grids and lists to record your ideas and key words that you might want to use.

Here's an example of a spider diagram about Perseus and Medusa:

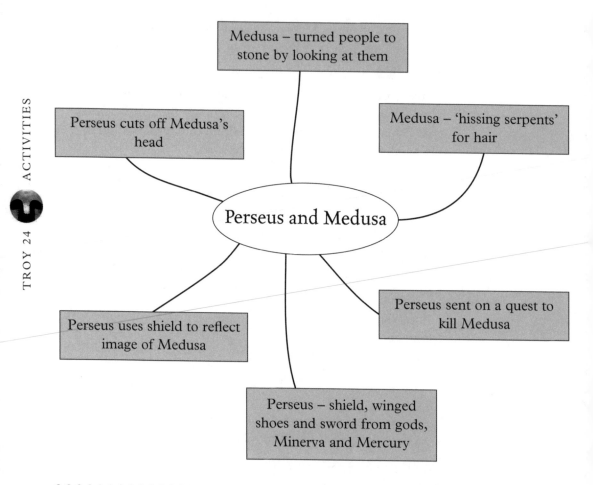

RETELLING

Step 1
Decide on an audience for your tale, for example, children.

Step 2
Decide on a form for your tale, for example, a poem or a short story. Think carefully about the 'voice' of your tale. It could be

formal or informal, written in American English or Standard English, or in a regional dialect.

Step 3

Jot down some appropriate words for your tale:

- Adjectives and nouns to describe the setting and characters
- Verbs and adverbs to describe the action
- Similes and metaphors to create interesting images in the reader's mind
- Alliteration (words starting with the same sounds) and rhymes (words ending with the same sounds), if writing a poem.

Step 4

Write a first draft of your tale.

Step 5

Swap your draft with a friend and ask for their comments.

Step 6

Write a final version of your tale, editing it until you feel it is the very best you can make it.

Further activities

1   The English language has lots of references to traditional tales, often in the form of common sayings and descriptions. Find out what the following mean:
    - 'Beware of Greeks bearing gifts.'
    - The girl was a 'Trojan horse' in the competition.
    - A Trojan virus.
    - Achilles heel.

2   Read about some other epic narrative tales. Find out what happened to Odysseus and Aeneas after the Trojan wars. Summarize one of their adventures.

3   Watch a 24-hour news channel for 15 minutes. Note down how many presenters, reporters, announcers and interviews there are. Discuss which parts give you most information, and which parts give you most entertainment.

4   Re-read Scene 15. Describe Helen's situation and her character. Debate whether Helen is to blame for the Trojan War or whether she is a victim of it.

5   Painters and sculptors through the ages have created images of characters in epic stories such as *The Iliad*. Make a collection of images, including film stills of the main characters, such as Achilles, Paris and Helen of Troy. Decide which one you feel best represents each character.

OXFORD Playscripts

Across the Barricades; Joan Lingard, adapted by David Ian Neville

Brother in the Land; Robert Swindells, adapted by Joe Standerline

Johnny and the Dead; Terry Pratchett, adapted by Stephen Briggs

The Amazing Maurice and his Educated Rodents; Terry Pratchett, adapted by Stephen Briggs

The Snake-stone; adapted from her own novel by Berlie Doherty

The Turbulent Term of Tyke Tiler; adapted from her own novel by Gene Kemp

The Demon Headmaster; Gillian Cross, adapted by Adrian Flynn

The Canterbury Tales; Geoffrey Chaucer, adapted by Martin Riley

Dracula; Bram Stoker, adapted by David Calcutt

Dr Faustus; Christopher Marlowe, adapted by Geraldine McCaughrean

Frankenstein; Mary Shelley, adapted by Philip Pullman

Lady Macbeth; David Calcutt

The Valley of Fear; Arthur Conan Doyle, adapted by Adrian Flynn

Troy 24; David Calcutt

The White Rose and the Swastika; Adrian Flynn

Salem; David Calcutt

For more information or to request your inspection copy of any of the Playscripts titles, please call customer services on +44 (0) 1536 741068